The Open University

MT365 Graphs, networks and design

Design 4

Block designs

Study guide

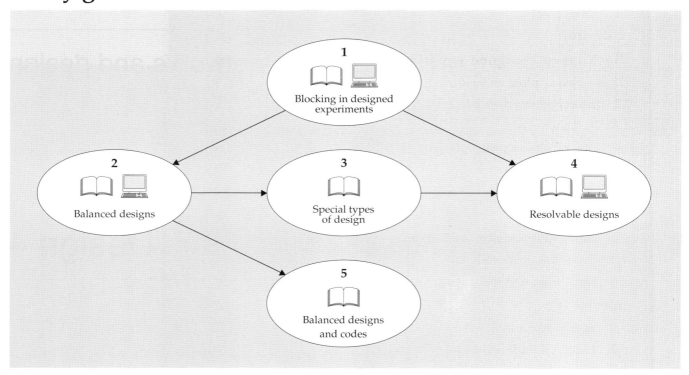

The most important sections of this unit are Sections 1 and 2, and you should make sure that you understand the main ideas of these sections. Section 2 discusses the important concept of a *balanced* design, and may take up more of your time than any other section. You should also make sure that you understand the concept of *resolvability*, introduced in Section 4.1; this concept is important in practical examples. Section 5 concerns block designs and codes, and provides a link with *Design 3*; if you are short of time, you may prefer just to skim through the main ideas and omit the details.

There are computer activities associated with Sections 1, 2 and 4. There is no audio-tape session or television programme associated with this unit.

The Open University, Walton Hall, Milton Keynes, MK7 6AA.

First published 1995. Second edition 2009.

Printed and bound by Page Bros, Norwich.

ISBN 978 0 7492 5424 7

2.1

The Open University has had Woodland Carbon Code Pending Issuance Units assigned from Doddington North forest creation project (IHS ID103/26819) that will, as the trees grow, compensate for the greenhouse gas emissions from the manufacture of the paper in MT365 Graphs, networks and design 4. More information can be found at https://www.woodlandcarboncode.org.uk/

Contents

Introduction

In *Design 1* we introduced the following example.

Suppose that we wish to design an experiment to test seven hay-fever drugs, called *Ampersand, Bastasneeze, Calamitine, Dripnomore, Eezybreathe, Fantastamine* and *Gladeyes*. Seven volunteers present themselves: Alex, Barbara, Chris, Deirdre, Eric, Fred and Gill. The hay-fever season is not long enough for each tester to try every drug, but it is desirable for each *pair* of drugs to be compared directly by some tester, so that the experiment is as 'balanced' as possible. We gave a solution in the form of a 'block table'. But how did we construct the table?

The answer to this question is given in Section 2.

In this unit we are concerned with the problem of designing experiments to compare various entities, such as hay-fever drugs or agricultural crops, as fairly as possible. Because the subject developed historically from design problems in agriculture, several of the terms and examples introduced in this unit have an agricultural flavour, but the subject can be applied to many other areas. Throughout the unit our emphasis is on the *construction* of good designs.

In Section 1, *Blocking in designed experiments,* we describe several types of experiment and introduce some basic terminology — in particular, the concept of an *incomplete block design*. We describe various difficulties that may arise in practice, and identify some features of a good design. We show how to associate a bipartite graph and an incidence matrix with a given block design, and explain why one requirement of a good design is that the associated graph be connected. We also describe some simple constructions for block designs and discuss their advantages and disadvantages.

In Section 2, *Balanced designs,* we introduce the concept of *concurrence*. This leads to the definition of an important type of design called a *balanced incomplete block design,* We show how to construct such designs, and how to derive new designs from existing ones.

In Section 3, *Special types of balanced design*, we describe two celebrated types of balanced design — *finite projective planes* and *Steiner triple systems.* The design proposed for the drug testing example in *Design 1* is an instance of both of these. We also discuss *latin squares* and show how they are used as designs in particular situations.

Section 4, *Resolvable designs,* is devoted to designs arising from experiments that divide naturally into 'harvests'. We analyse the properties of such designs, and describe some constructions, including the use of latin squares.

Finally, in Section 5, *Balanced designs and codes,* we show how to construct codes from balanced incomplete block designs.

1 Blocking in designed experiments

Every year many hundreds of agricultural trials are held to compare new varieties of cereal and vegetable crops. Plant breeders may spend several years developing a new variety that may be more resistant to disease, give a bigger yield, or have some other advantage. These varieties are submitted for testing by independent bodies, who conduct trials at several sites. As a result of these trials, a recommended list of varieties is published each year.

Inclusion in the recommended list tends to increase the sale of seeds of any particular variety, so the breeders are anxious that the varieties they submit be judged fairly. Those running the trials are also concerned about this, for if a poor variety is recommended it may be grown by many farmers and produce a national decrease in the yield from that crop. So how are the different varieties compared?

1.1 Varieties, plots and blocks

We begin with some basic definitions.

Definitions

In an experiment, the **varieties** are the items being compared.

A **plot** is a unit of experimental material on which a single variety is tested.

A **block** is a group of plots which are similar in the sense that, if the same variety is tested on each, then similar results can be expected.

Plots are often defined by boundaries of space or time; for example, in an agricultural experiment each plot may be a part of a field on which a particular variety of wheat is tested.

We now illustrate the wide range of examples for which block designs are appropriate.

Example 1.1: wheat testing

In an agricultural experiment, there are six varieties of winter wheat, and four different sites where the types of wheat are grown. Ideally, all six varieties should be grown on all four sites, but each site has space for only three or four varieties.

We represent this experiment by a block table with six *varieties A, B, C, D, E* and *F* (corresponding to the varieties of wheat) and four *blocks* 1, 2, 3, 4 (corresponding to the sites); each block contains three or four *plots*, giving fourteen plots altogether:

1	2	3	4
A	A	B	C
B	D	E	D
C	E	F	F
D	F		

The order of the letters within each column does not matter.

■

Example 1.2: pig-feed testing

A farmer wishes to discover the effects of different feeds upon the growth of piglets. Here, the *varieties* are the feeds and the *plots* are the piglets. Sows commonly produce ten or more piglets to a litter, and there may well be inherent differences between different litters, so it is sensible to treat the litters as *blocks*.

■

It would not be appropriate to apply this reasoning to animals like cows, which rarely produce more than one calf at a time.

Example 1.3: cake-additive testing

A bakery firm wishes to test the effect on cake quality of combinations of two additives — glycerine (in three different amounts), and tartaric acid (in four different amounts). Here, the *varieties* are the $4 \times 3 = 12$ different combinations of glycerine and tartaric acid. The bakery has three large commercial ovens, each of which can be used twice a day. In order not to disrupt production, only one day is set aside for the experiment, and there are six different bakings, two per oven. Each oven has room for six large trays of cakes. The bakers claim that a whole trayful of cakes is needed to assess each cake mixture, and so each tray has a single variety. Thus the trays are the *plots*, and the bakings are the *blocks*, each containing six plots.

■

The ovens could also be taken as a larger sort of block, each containing two bakings.

Example 1.4: clinical trials

In a clinical trial, a new drug is compared with a standard one to see which is more successful in treating a certain disease. The trial is carried out on all patients with the disease at a given hospital over a period of several months. Here, the *varieties* are the two drugs, and the *plots* are the patients. Even if the patients all come from the same part of the country, and have the same general medical care in hospital, they may still be disparate, and so the experimenter should think of dividing them into blocks. One possibility is to group the patients into ten-year age bands; another is to divide them according to how severely they have the disease. ■

Example 1.5: fertilizer testing

An agricultural experiment is carried out to determine the amounts of nitrogen, potash and phosphate that combine to give a good fertilizer for sugar-beet. Four different amounts of nitrogen are chosen, together with two amounts of potash and two of phosphate, giving $4 \times 2 \times 2 = 16$ possible fertilizers altogether. These sixteen fertilizers are the *varieties*. The sugar-beet is grown in a single field which is split up into *plots* (in the usual sense of the word), each plot being treated by one of the fertilizers. These plots may vary in fertility across the field. There are several possible reasons for this: for example, one part of the field may have had waste material dumped on it in the past; one edge of the field may be shaded by trees or contaminated with fumes from a neighbouring road; drainage patterns may vary across the field, as there may be an underground stream. However, it is likely that neighbouring plots are similar, and so the *blocks* are taken to be groups of neighbouring plots. ■

The above examples illustrate several different reasons for blocking. In Examples 1.1 and 1.2, the experimenters want results that apply to more than just one site or litter, and so they deliberately use heterogeneous plots, but allow for that heterogeneity in their analysis. Scientists want their results to apply to very precise conditions, and wish to be able to control their experimental material accordingly. Outside the laboratory, such control is not always possible, as Example 1.5 shows. Even when it is theoretically possible to make all the plots similar, it may be financially or operationally infeasible to do so. For example, in clinical trials (Example 1.4), the experimenter has to accept the patients who have contracted the disease, rather than choose a homogeneous group of people to infect with the disease!

These examples also show that there are two, rather different, sorts of block. Sites and litters have 'natural' boundaries: if the sites or litters are taken as blocks, it is clear when two plots are in the same block and when they are not. But if patients are put into blocks according to age, or plots in the field are grouped into blocks of neighbouring plots, then it is no longer clear where the block boundaries should be. If the field is a long thin strip, then the blocks will be lengths of the strip, but only experience with the type of experiment can suggest what a good size for the block should be.

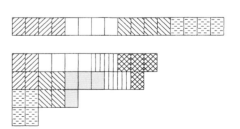

In some experiments, the blocks are of different sizes. For instance, in Example 1.1 blocks 1 and 2 contain four varieties, but blocks 3 and 4 contain only three, and in Example 1.2 not all sows produce the same number of piglets. In such cases, we can sometimes achieve blocks of the same size simply by ignoring a few plots in the over-large blocks. However, in all the designs of interest to us, the situation where the blocks contain different numbers of varieties does not arise.

1.2 Incomplete block designs

In Example 1.1, we dismissed the case in which each variety of wheat is grown at each site, since sufficient space is usually not available. In a situation in which every variety *does* occur once in each block, we say that the blocks are *complete*. Although there may be problems of procedure and analysis connected with such experiments, there are no *design* problems involved, and so we shall not consider such experiments further.

More usual is the situation where each block is too small to hold every variety; in such a case, each block is *incomplete*. We shall use the following definition and notation.

Definition

An **incomplete block design** consists of the following:

- a set of **varieties**;

- a set of **blocks**, each containing the same number of varieties;

- a list showing the varieties allocated to the plots in each block.

No block contains every variety, and no block contains any variety more than once.

Notation

v denotes the number of varieties;

b denotes the number of blocks;

k denotes the **block size** — the number of plots in each block.

We frequently abbreviate *incomplete block design* to *block design*, or simply *design*, when there is no possibility of confusion.

Since the block design is incomplete, no block can contain every variety, and so v and k always satisfy the inequality

$$k < v.$$

From now on we shall consider incomplete block designs as defined above and use some of the terms introduced earlier more generally. Often it is convenient to think of a block table as a mathematical entity in its own right, so we shall refer to a block table in which each block consists of k objects chosen from the same set as a *block design* and use the terms *variety* and *plot* when they do not necessarily have the experimental interpretation of our original definition.

Example 1.6: hay-fever drug testing

In *Design 1* we presented the following solution to the problem of testing hay-fever drugs:

Alex	should test	*Ampersand, Bastasneeze* and *Dripnomore*;
Barbara	should test	*Bastasneeze, Calamitine* and *Eezybreathe*;
Chris	should test	*Calamitine, Dripnomore* and *Fantastamine*;
Deirdre	should test	*Dripnomore, Eezybreathe* and *Gladeyes*;
Eric	should test	*Eezybreathe, Fantastamine* and *Ampersand*;
Fred	should test	*Fantastamine, Gladeyes* and *Bastasneeze*;
Gill	should test	*Gladeyes, Ampersand* and *Calamatine*.

We represented the above assignment of drugs to testers by a block table consisting of seven columns, corresponding to the seven testers. The entries in each column are the drugs assigned to the particular tester; for example, column $\mathbb{C}$ (corresponding to Chris) consists of the three drugs C, D and F (*Calamitine, Dripnomore* and *Fantastamine*).

A	B	C	D	E	F	G
A	*B*	*C*	*D*	*E*	*F*	*G*
B	*C*	*D*	*E*	*F*	*G*	*A*
D	*E*	*F*	*G*	*A*	*B*	*C*

In this example, $v = 7$, $b = 7$ and $k = 3$. ◼

We use italic letters to represent the varieties — the drugs — and outline letters to represent the blocks — the sets of drugs assigned to the testers.

Example 1.7: hay-fever drug testing

Another way of describing the experiment to test hay fever drugs is as follows.

Ampersand	is tested by	*Alex, Eric* and *Gill*;
Bastasneeze	is tested by	*Alex, Barbara* and *Fred*;
Calamitine	is tested by	*Barbara, Chris* and *Gill*;
Dripnomore	is tested by	*Alex, Chris* and *Deirdre*;
Eezybreathe	is tested by	*Barbara, Deirdre* and *Eric*;
Fantastamine	is tested by	*Chris, Eric* and *Fred*;
Gladeyes	is tested by	*Deirdre, Fred* and *Gill*.

We thus obtain the following block design:

A	B	C	D	E	F	G
A	*A*	*B*	*A*	*B*	*C*	*D*
E	*B*	*C*	*C*	*D*	*E*	*F*
G	*F*	*G*	*D*	*E*	*F*	*G*

Here we again use italic letters to represent the varieties — the testers — and outline letters to represent the blocks — the sets of testers of each drug.

In this example, we again have $v = 7$, $b = 7$ and $k = 3$. ◼

Problem 1.1

Write down the values of v, b and k for each of the following block designs:

(a)

1	2	3	4
1	2	3	4
3	4	1	5
5	3	2	1

(b)

1	2	3	4	5	6
A	*C*	*G*	*E*	*D*	*I*
G	*D*	*B*	*F*	*H*	*B*
E	*H*	*A*	*I*	*C*	*F*

Consider next the following block design:

1	2	3	4
A	*A*	*B*	*C*
B	*B*	*E*	*D*
C	*E*	*F*	*E*

The trouble with this block design is that the varieties do not occur the same number of times. For example, varieties B and E appear three times each, whereas varieties D and F appear only once. If all of the varieties under examination have the same status or importance, then it is desirable that each occurs the same number of times. However, this is not always possible; for example, one plant breeder might supply very few seeds of one variety, and much information would be lost if *all* the varieties under test were limited to this same small amount.

In this unit, we are interested only in designs in which each variety occurs the same number of times.

Definition

A block design is **equi-replicate** if each variety occurs the same number of times; this number is the **replication**, and is denoted by r.

For example, the designs in Examples 1.6 and 1.7 are both equi-replicate with $r = 3$.

Problem 1.2 ————————————————————

Decide whether each of the block designs of Problem 1.1 is equi-replicate; if so, write down the value of r.

The letters v, b, r and k are in standard use by combinatorialists, and are often called the *parameters* of the block design.

For convenience, we summarize our assumptions about the four parameters.

The **var**iety letters are **v** and **r**, and the **b**lock letters are **b** and **k**.

Many experimenters and statisticians use the letter t instead of v, and refer to varieties as *treatments*, since the varieties may refer to drugs used to treat patients (Example 1.4) or to fertilizers used to treat plants (Example 1.5).

Summary

In this unit, all incomplete block designs are assumed to be equi-replicate, with the following **parameters**:

- v varieties
- b blocks
- k varieties in each block, where $k < v$
- r occurrences of each variety.

There are various relationships between these parameters. In Examples 1.6 and 1.7, we have

$$v = 7, \quad b = 7, \quad r = 3, \quad k = 3,$$

so, for these designs,

$$vr = bk.$$

The following theorem shows that this equation holds for any equi-replicate incomplete block design.

Theorem 1.1

In an equi-replicate incomplete block design, the parameters v, r, b and k are related by the equation

$$vr = bk.$$

Proof

There are v varieties, each of which occurs in r plots, and so the total number of plots is vr.

We use the technique of counting something in two different ways.

Also, there are b blocks, each containing k plots, and so the total number of plots is bk.

Hence

$$vr = bk.$$ ∎

Problem 1.3

Write down the values of v, r, b and k for each of the following equi-replicate designs, and verify that $vr = bk$ in each case:

(a)

1	2	3	4	5	6
A	C	G	E	D	I
G	D	B	F	H	B
E	H	A	I	C	F

(b)

A	B	C	D	E	F	G
A	B	C	D	E	F	G
B	C	D	E	F	G	A
D	E	F	G	A	B	C

Isomorphic designs

Sometimes we need to decide when two designs are essentially the same and when they are different. To see what we mean by this, consider the following designs:

1	2	3	4		1	2	3	4
A	A	B	C		A	A	B	C
B	D	E	D		B	C	E	D
C	E	F	F		D	F	F	E

Although these designs are not the *same*, they are closely related. If in the first design we interchange the varieties C and D and the varieties E and F, then we obtain the second design. This leads to the following definition.

Definition

Two block designs are **isomorphic** if one can be obtained from the other by relabelling the blocks and/or the varieties.

Examples of two non-isomorphic designs are given at the beginning of Section 2.

For many purposes, we can consider isomorphic designs as interchangeable. For example, if an experimenter requires a block design for six varieties in four blocks of size 3, with each variety occurring twice, we do not need to give both the above isomorphic designs. However, if the experimenter also specifies that the particular varieties A and E must occur together in some block, then only the first of the above designs is of interest.

Problem 1.4

Show, by relabelling the blocks and varieties **in** design (a), that the following two block designs are isomorphic:

(a)

A	B	C	D	E	F	G
0	1	2	3	4	5	6
1	2	3	4	5	6	0
3	4	5	6	0	1	2

(b)

1	2	3	4	5	6	7
Y	W	T	H	R	W	H
E	H	R	E	A	E	A
A	Y	Y	R	W	T	T

1.3   Incidence

Connected designs

In general, the analysis of experiments conducted in incomplete blocks is too complicated to discuss in detail here, but we can observe enough about it to appreciate some aspects of good design. For example, consider the following incomplete block design with parameters $v = b = 8$ and $k = r = 2$.

1	2	3	4	5	6	7	8
A	C	B	A	F	D	F	G
B	E	C	D	G	E	H	H

If this design were used for an experiment, we could use it to compare some pairs of varieties, but not others. For example,

- varieties A and B both occur in block 1, and therefore can be compared *directly*.

- varieties A and C do not occur in the same block, and so cannot be compared directly; however, varieties A and B can be compared directly in block 1, and varieties B and C can be compared directly in block 3, and these two direct comparisons can then be combined to give an *indirect* comparison of varieties A and C.

- no amount of indirect comparison connects varieties A and F, and so this design cannot be used for comparing them.

It follows that, if our purpose is to compare as many pairs of varieties as possible, then this is not a good design.

The following terms are useful when we need to discuss comparisons between varieties.

Definitions

Two varieties are **directly comparable** if there is a block that contains both.

Two varieties A and B are **indirectly comparable** if there is a chain of varieties $A_1, \ldots, A_n$ such that A and A_1, A_1 and A_2, ..., and A_n and B are all directly comparable.

A block design is **connected** if each pair of varieties is directly or indirectly comparable.

In the above example, the varieties A and B are directly comparable and the varieties A and C are indirectly comparable. The design is not connected, since the varieties A and F are neither directly nor indirectly comparable.

In general, we regard *connectedness* as an important requirement of a good design. With this criterion, the above design is not a good design.

Problem 1.5 ───────────────────────────────

In the above example, decide whether the following pairs of varieties are directly or indirectly comparable:

(a)   varieties F and H;

(b)   varieties C and G;

(c)   varieties A and E.

Problem 1.6

Construct a *connected* design with the same parameters as the above design.

The use of the word *connected* recalls the definition of a connected graph.

We can associate a bipartite graph with an incomplete block design by drawing a vertex for each variety and a vertex for each block, and drawing an edge between a variety-vertex and a block-vertex whenever the corresponding variety is contained in the corresponding block. For example, the graph of the above design is shown in the margin.

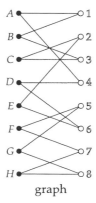

1	2	3	4	5	6	7	8
A	C	B	A	F	D	F	G
B	E	C	D	G	E	H	H

design

graph

Two varieties are directly or indirectly comparable whenever the corresponding vertices are connected by a path. It follows that

- a design is connected if and only if the associated bipartite graph is connected.

Since the bipartite graph for the above design is disconnected, the design is not a connected design.

For example, there is no path from vertex *E* to vertex *F*.

Problem 1.7

By drawing the associated bipartite graphs, determine whether the following designs are connected.

(a)

1	2	3	4
A	A	B	C
B	D	E	D
C	E	F	F

(b)

1	2	3	4	5	6
A	C	G	E	D	I
G	D	B	F	H	B
E	H	A	I	C	F

Incidence matrices

In Example 1.7, the drug testing example, we can represent the information about who tests which drugs by the following incidence matrix, in which the entry in row i and column j is 1 if volunteer i tests drug j, and 0 otherwise.

	A	B	C	D	E	F	G
Alex	1	1	0	1	0	0	0
Barbara	0	1	1	0	1	0	0
Chris	0	0	1	1	0	1	0
Deirdre	0	0	0	1	1	0	1
Eric	1	0	0	0	1	1	0
Fred	0	1	0	0	0	1	1
Gill	1	0	1	0	0	0	1

This is the incidence matrix used in *Design 1*.

For block designs in general, we adopt the following corresponding definition.

Definition

The **incidence matrix B** of a block design with v varieties and b blocks is the $v \times b$ matrix with rows labelled by the varieties and columns labelled by the blocks, in which the entry in row A and column $\mathbb{B}$ is

  1,   if variety A lies in block $\mathbb{B}$;

  0,   if variety A does not lie in block $\mathbb{B}$.

This matrix is the matrix that we obtain if we regard the design as an incidence structure.

Two block designs are isomorphic if and only if we can permute the rows and/or columns of the incidence matrix of one design to get the incidence matrix of the other.

Problem 1.8

Write down the incidence matrix of each of the following block designs.

(a)

1	2	3	4	5	6
A	C	G	E	D	I
G	D	B	F	H	B
E	H	A	I	C	F

(b)

A	B	C	D	E	F	G
A	B	C	D	E	F	G
B	C	D	E	F	G	A
D	E	F	G	A	B	C

This is the design in Example 1.6.

1.4   Constructions for block designs

We now describe some methods for constructing block designs. Some of these constructions start from scratch, whereas others derive new block designs from existing ones.

All-combinations method

Suppose that the numbers v and k are specified, where $k < v$. The following construction yields a design called an *unreduced design*.

All-combinations method

For the blocks, take all possible combinations of k varieties chosen from the set of v varieties.

For example, for $v = 4$ and $k = 2$, there are six possible combinations of 2 varieties chosen from the set of 4 varieties. If the varieties are A, B, C and D, these combinations are AB, AC, AD, BC, BD and CD, giving rise to the following design:

1	2	3	4	5	6
A	A	A	B	B	C
B	C	D			

Advantage   This method is very simple and (in some sense) symmetrical.

Disadvantage Since the number of blocks is the binomial coefficient $\binom{v}{k}$, $\quad \binom{v}{k} = v!\,/\,k!(v-k)!$

which increases rapidly as v increases, the number of blocks is large unless either k or $v-k$ is very small. In many experimental situations there are not as many blocks as this available.

Problem 1.9

Use the all-combinations method to construct:

(a) an unreduced design with varieties A, B, C, D and E, and block-size 2;

(b) an unreduced design with varieties A, B, C, D and E, and block-size 3.

Circle construction

Suppose that the numbers v and k are specified, where $k < v$. The following construction yields a design with $b = v$ and $r = k$.

> ## Circle construction
>
> Place the letters representing the varieties around a circle, and mark a starting point;
>
> for the first block, take the first k varieties, proceeding clockwise from the starting point;
>
> for the second block, take the next k varieties, still proceeding clockwise;
>
> and so on.

For example, for $v = 7$ and $k = 3$, we obtain the following design:

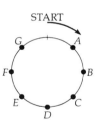

1	2	3	4	5	6	7
A	D	G	C	F	B	E
B	E	A	D	G	C	F
C	F	B	E	A	D	G

Advantage This method can be used for any values of v and k for which $k < v$.

Disadvantage This method does not always produce good designs; for example, if v is divisible by k, then the design is not connected.

Problem 1.10

Use the circle construction to obtain an incomplete block design with six varieties A, B, C, D, E and F, six blocks and block-size 4. Is the design connected?

Cyclic construction

This is the most useful construction in this subsection, and will be used throughout the rest of this unit.

Suppose that the numbers v and k are specified, where $k < v$. The following construction yields a *cyclic design* with $b = v$ and $r = k$.

Cyclic construction

Denote the varieties by 0, 1, ..., $v - 1$;

for the first block, choose any k of these integers;

for the second block, add 1 to each variety in the first block, replacing v by 0 if it occurs;

for the third block, add 1 to each variety in the second block, replacing v by 0 if it occurs;

and so on.

For example, for $v = 6$ and $k = 3$, we label the varieties 0, 1, 2, 3, 4, 5. Let us choose the first block to be 0 1 4; then the second block is 1 2 5 and the third block is 2 3 0 (on replacing 6 by 0). Continuing in this way, we obtain the following design:

1	2	3	4	5	6
0	1	2	3	4	5
1	2	3	4	5	0
4	5	0	1	2	3

When the varieties are letters, rather than numbers, the construction is similar. For example, if the varieties are A, B, C, D, E, F and the first block is chosen to be $A\ B\ E$, then the second block is $B\ C\ F$ and the third block is $C\ D\ A$ (on replacing G by A). Continuing in this way, we obtain the following design:

1	2	3	4	5	6
A	B	C	D	E	F
B	C	D	E	F	A
E	F	A	B	C	D

Advantages and disadvantages

Some cyclic designs are very good and some are very bad, depending on the choice of the first block. Some choices of the first block may give designs that are not connected. Also some choices of the first block can lead to the nth block being the same as the first block, for some $n < b$; the $(n+1)$th block is then the same as the second, and so on. In such a case, the whole design consists of a number of copies of the first $n - 1$ blocks, which form an incomplete block design in their own right.

Problem 1.11 ───────────────────────────────

In each of the following cases, construct a cyclic block design, and state whether it is connected:

(a) $v = 7$, $k = 3$,   first block 0 1 3;

(b) $v = 6$, $k = 3$,   first block 1 3 5;

(c) $v = 6$, $k = 4$,   first block $A\ C\ D\ F$.

New designs from old

The following two methods are useful ways of constructing new designs from existing designs.

Complement of a design

From a given design Δ, the **complement** $\overline{\Delta}$ is constructed as follows.

For each block $\mathbb{B}$ of Δ, construct a block $\overline{\mathbb{B}}$ of $\overline{\Delta}$ by taking the varieties in block $\overline{\mathbb{B}}$ of $\overline{\Delta}$ to be those varieties that do not occur in block $\mathbb{B}$ of Δ.

It follows from the definition that the complement of $\overline{\Delta}$ is Δ

For example, let Δ be the design

1	2	3	4	5	6	7
A	B	C	D	E	F	G
B	C	D	E	F	G	A
D	E	F	G	A	B	C

then $\overline{\Delta}$ is the design

1	2	3	4	5	6	7
C	A	A	A	B	A	B
E	D	B	B	C	C	D
F	F	E	C	D	D	E
G	G	G	F	G	E	F

Problem 1.12

Construct the complement of the design:

1	2	3	4	5
0	1	1	0	0
1	3	2	2	3
2	4	3	4	4

Problem 1.13

A design Δ has parameters v, b, r and k. Find the corresponding parameters $\overline{v}$, $\overline{b}$, $\overline{r}$ and $\overline{k}$ of the complement $\overline{\Delta}$, and verify that they also satisfy Theorem 1.1.

Dual of a design

From a given design Δ, the **dual** Δ^* is constructed as follows.

Interchange the roles of varieties and blocks, re-interpreting 'contains' as 'occurs in', and *vice versa.*

The dual of a design is a special case of the dual of an incidence structure, defined in *Design 1.*

It follows from the definition that the dual of Δ^* is Δ.

For example, let Δ be the design

1	2	3	4
A	A	B	C
B	D	E	D
C	E	F	F

then Δ^* is the design

A	B	C	D	E	F
1	1	1	2	2	3
2	3	4	4	3	4

Notice also that the designs given in Examples 1.6 and 1.7 are duals of each other.

Note that the bipartite graph of the dual design Δ^* is the same as that of the original design Δ, except that the two sets of vertices corresponding to the varieties and blocks are interchanged. If this graph is connected, then so are both designs. If it is not connected, then neither are the two designs. It follows that Δ *is connected if and only if* Δ^* *is connected*.

Problem 1.14

Construct the dual of the design:

1	2	3	4	5	6	7	8	9	10
A	B	C	D	E	A	B	C	D	E
B	C	D	E	A	C	D	E	A	B
F	F	F	F	F	D	E	A	B	C

Problem 1.15

A design Δ has parameters v, b, r and k. Find the corresponding parameters v^*, b^*, r^* and k^* of the dual Δ^*, and verify that they also satisfy Theorem 1.1.

1.5 Computer activities

The computer activities for this section are described in the *Computer Activities Booklet*.

After studying this section, you should be able to:

- appreciate the nature and importance of blocking in different experimental situations;

- explain the terms *variety, plot, block, incomplete block design, equi-replicate design* and *replication*;

- explain the meanings of the parameters *v, r, b* and *k*, and prove that in an equi-replicate incomplete block design with equal block sizes $vr = bk$;

- construct the *bipartite graph* and the *incidence matrix* associated with a given design, and test whether a given design is *connected*;

- construct *unreduced, circle* and *cyclic* designs, and the *complement* and *dual* of a given design.

---

2 Balanced designs

In this section we describe some other ways of representing incomplete block designs. In particular, we construct *concurrence* matrices and use them to find the *concurrences* in a design; these can be used to assess the design. When the concurrences are all equal, we have a *balanced design* — such designs are important, both structurally and in practice. Finally, we describe some useful methods for constructing certain balanced designs.

2.1 Concurrence

Consider an experiment in which we wish to compare seven varieties, A, B, C, D, E, F and G. Two cyclic designs that we could use are the following:

Design 1 is the design in Example 1.6.

1	2	3	4	5	6	7		1	2	3	4	5	6	7
A	B	C	D	E	F	G		A	B	C	D	E	F	G
B	C	D	E	F	G	A		B	C	D	E	F	G	A
D	E	F	G	A	B	C		C	D	E	F	G	A	B
			design 1								design 2			

At first sight, these designs may appear similar, but the differences between them become apparent when we try to compare any variety with the other varieties.

Problem 2.1

For each of these designs, write down the number of blocks in which variety A is compared directly with

(a)   variety B;   (b)   variety C;   (c)   variety D.

Comment on your results.

In answering Problem 2.1, you will have found that the two designs give different results. In design 1, each pair of varieties are compared together in exactly one block. However, in design 2, variety A is compared twice with varieties B and G, once with varieties C and F, and never with varieties D and E. It does seem that design 1 provides a fairer comparison of the varieties. Indeed, it looks as though our aim should be to find designs in which all comparisons occur the same number of times.

This idea leads to the following definitions.

Definition

Let A and B be two distinct varieties in an incomplete block design. The **concurrence** of A and B is the number of blocks in which both A and B occur, and is denoted by λ_{AB} .

For example,

in design 1, $\lambda_{AB} = \lambda_{AC} = \lambda_{AD} = 1$;

in design 2, $\lambda_{AB} = 2$, $\lambda_{AC} = 1$, $\lambda_{AD} = 0$.

It can be shown that, among all incomplete block designs with a given replication and block size, the differences between the varieties are estimated most precisely when all the concurrences are equal. Designs with this property have a special name.

Definition

An incomplete block design Δ is **balanced** if there is a constant number λ such that each pair of distinct varieties of Δ occur together in exactly λ blocks.

The number λ is the **concurrence** of the balanced design Δ.

It is standard practice to use the Greek letter λ for the concurrence of a balanced block design.

For example, design 1 is a balanced design with concurrence $\lambda = 1$, whereas design 2 is not balanced.

Decide whether each of the following designs is balanced; if so, write down the concurrence λ.

(a)

1	2	3	4	5	6	7	8	9
A	B	C	D	E	A	A	B	C
B	C	D	E	F	F	E	D	F

(b)

1	2	3	4	5	6	7	8	9	10
A	B	C	D	E	A	B	C	D	E
B	C	D	E	A	C	D	E	A	B
F	F	F	F	F	D	E	A	B	C

In investigating concurrences, it is convenient to introduce the *concurrence matrix*.

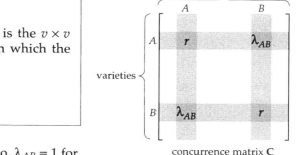

varieties

concurrence matrix **C**

Definition

The **concurrence matrix C** of an incomplete block design is the $v \times v$ matrix with rows and columns labelled by the varieties, in which the entry in row A and column B is

r if the varieties A and B are the same;

λ_{AB} if the varieties A and B are different.

For example, for design 1, $r = 3$ so each diagonal entry is 3; also, $\lambda_{AB} = 1$ for all pairs of varieties A and B, so the non-diagonal entries are all 1:

$$
\begin{array}{c|ccccccc}
 & A & B & C & D & E & F & G \\
\hline
A & 3 & 1 & 1 & 1 & 1 & 1 & 1 \\
B & 1 & 3 & 1 & 1 & 1 & 1 & 1 \\
C & 1 & 1 & 3 & 1 & 1 & 1 & 1 \\
D & 1 & 1 & 1 & 3 & 1 & 1 & 1 \\
E & 1 & 1 & 1 & 1 & 3 & 1 & 1 \\
F & 1 & 1 & 1 & 1 & 1 & 3 & 1 \\
G & 1 & 1 & 1 & 1 & 1 & 1 & 3
\end{array}
$$

For design 2, $r = 3$ so each diagonal entry is 3; also, $\lambda_{AB} = 2$, $\lambda_{AC} = 1$ and $\lambda_{AD} = 0$; indeed, each non-diagonal entry is either 0, 1 or 2:

$$
\begin{array}{c|ccccccc}
 & A & B & C & D & E & F & G \\
\hline
A & 3 & 2 & 1 & 0 & 0 & 1 & 2 \\
B & 2 & 3 & 2 & 1 & 0 & 0 & 1 \\
C & 1 & 2 & 3 & 2 & 1 & 0 & 0 \\
D & 0 & 1 & 2 & 3 & 2 & 1 & 0 \\
E & 0 & 0 & 1 & 2 & 3 & 2 & 1 \\
F & 1 & 0 & 0 & 1 & 2 & 3 & 2 \\
G & 2 & 1 & 0 & 0 & 1 & 2 & 3
\end{array}
$$

More generally, the concurrence matrix of a balanced design with replication r and concurrence λ has diagonal entries r and non-diagonal entries λ. This means that the concurrence matrix has the form shown in the margin.

$$
\mathbf{C} = \begin{bmatrix}
r & \lambda & \lambda & \dots & \lambda & \lambda \\
\lambda & r & \lambda & \dots & \lambda & \lambda \\
\lambda & \lambda & r & \dots & \lambda & \lambda \\
\cdot & \cdot & \cdot & \dots & \cdot & \cdot \\
\lambda & \lambda & \lambda & \dots & r & \lambda \\
\lambda & \lambda & \lambda & \dots & \lambda & r
\end{bmatrix}
$$

Problem 2.3

Write down the concurrence matrix of the design:

1	2	3	4
A	A	B	C
B	D	E	D
C	E	F	F

Is it a balanced design?

There is an interesting connection between incidence matrices and concurrence matrices. The following problem indicates this connection.

Problem 2.4

For each of the designs 1 and 2, write down

(a)   the concurrence matrix $\mathbf{C}$;

(b)   the incidence matrix $\mathbf{B}$ and its transpose $\mathbf{B}^T$;

(c)   the product matrix $\mathbf{BB}^T$.

Comment on your results.

The matrix $\mathbf{B}^T$ is the *transpose* of $\mathbf{B}$ — the matrix obtained from $\mathbf{B}$ by interchanging the rows and columns.

The result of Problem 2.4 is illustrated by the following diagrams.

The matrix product $\mathbf{BB}^T$ is

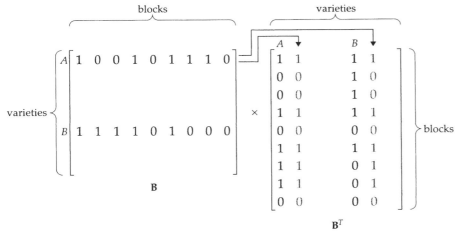

The grey columns are inserted to show how the elements in columns A and B of row A of the matrix product are calculated.

The concurrence matrix $\mathbf{C}$ is

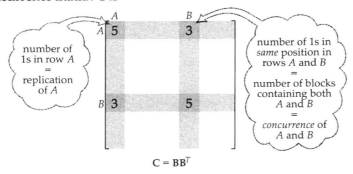

$$\mathbf{C} = \mathbf{BB}^T$$

The result of Problem 2.4 holds for any incomplete block design.

Theorem 2.1

The concurrence matrix $\mathbf{C}$ of an incomplete block design is $\mathbf{BB}^T$, where $\mathbf{B}$ is the incidence matrix of the design.

Note that, if A is any variety, then

the replication of A = the number of 1s in row A of **B**

= the corresponding diagonal entry of $\mathbf{BB}^T = \mathbf{C}$.

Also, if A and B are different varieties, then

λ_{AB} = the number of blocks containing both A and B

= the number of 1s in the same position in rows A and B of **B**

= the corresponding non-diagonal entry of the matrix $\mathbf{BB}^T = \mathbf{C}$.

We return to concurrence matrices in Section 2.3.

2.2 Balanced incomplete block designs

Recall that a design with equal block sizes is *balanced* if all its concurrences are equal. Such balanced incomplete block designs occur frequently; they are often abbreviated to BIBDs.

The following theorem gives an equation relating the parameters v, r, k and λ in a BIBD.

Theorem 2.2

Let Δ be a balanced incomplete block design with v varieties, replication r, block size k, and concurrence λ. Then

$$\lambda(v - 1) = r(k - 1).$$

Proof

Let A be a variety of Δ, and consider the number of plots that occur in blocks containing variety A. There are r such blocks, and each has k plots, so this number is rk.

Again, we use the technique of counting something in two different ways.

We now look at the varieties that occur in these plots. Variety A occurs r times. Each variety other than A occurs λ times in the same block as A, and so occurs λ times in the plots we are considering. Since there are $v - 1$ varieties other than A, the total number of plots is $r + \lambda(v - 1)$.

Equating these results, we have

$$r + \lambda(v - 1) = rk,$$

and so

$$\lambda(v - 1) = rk - r = r(k - 1). \qquad \blacksquare$$

Theorem 2.2 tells us that, for any balanced design, $\lambda = r(k - 1)/(v - 1)$. It follows that any design in which $r(k - 1)/(v - 1)$ is not an integer cannot be a balanced design.

Problem 2.5 ────────────────────

For each of the following balanced designs, verify that $\lambda(v - 1) = r(k - 1)$.

(a)

1	2	3	4	5	6	7
0	1	2	3	4	5	6
1	2	3	4	5	6	0
3	4	5	6	0	1	2

(b)

1	2	3	4	5	6	7	8	9	10
A	B	C	D	E	A	B	C	D	E
B	C	D	E	A	C	D	E	A	B
F	F	F	F	F	D	E	A	B	C

(c)	1	2	3	4	5	6	7	8	9	10	11	12	13	14
	1	2	3	4	5	6	7	3	4	5	6	7	1	2
	2	3	4	5	6	7	1	5	6	7	1	2	3	4
	4	5	6	7	1	2	3	6	7	1	2	3	4	5
	8	8	8	8	8	8	8	7	1	2	3	4	5	6

Warning Do not jump to hasty conclusions about a design from the properties of its parameters. For example, the parameters of designs 1 and 2 ($v = 7$, $b = 7$, $r = 3$, $k = 3$) satisfy all the conditions

$$k < v, \quad vr = bk, \quad r(k-1)/(v-1) \text{ is an integer,}$$

but design 2 is not balanced.

These conditions are *necessary* for a balanced design: they are not *sufficient*.

In fact, it is possible to find integers v, b, r and k satisfying these conditions, for which *no* BIBD exists, as the following example shows.

Example 2.1

Let $v = 16$, $r = 3$, $b = 8$, $k = 6$. Then

$$k < v, \quad vr = 48 = bk, \quad r(k-1)/(v-1) = (3 \times 5)/15 = 1,$$
$$\text{which is an integer.}$$

So it looks as though it should be possible to have a BIBD with the given parameters with $\lambda = 1$. But suppose that one block of such a design contains the varieties A, B, C, D, E and F. Since $\lambda = 1$, the varieties B, C, D, E and F never occur again with A or with each other. But $r = 3$, and so there are three blocks containing A and five blocks not containing A. Since these five blocks not containing A must contain all further occurrences of B, C, D, E and F (which, moreover, never occur together again), each of the five varieties B, C, D, E and F must occur in a separate single block. This means that each of these varieties can occur only twice, contradicting the fact that $r = 3$. It follows that no BIBD exists with these parameters. ■

Historical note

Balanced incomplete block designs were introduced by Frank Yates in 1936. He employed the notation we have used here, except that, like most statisticians, he wrote t instead of v. Yates' original paper contains the comment that an exhaustive search had shown that there is no BIBD with $v = 16$, $b = 8$, $r = 3$, $k = 6$.

Our next theorem explains why we cannot find a BIBD with $v = 16$ and $b = 8$. We can now dismiss such cases quickly, because $b < v$, but Fisher's inequality was not known in 1936 when Frank Yates discussed the problem.

If you look back at the BIBDs you have met so far, you will notice that in each case the number of blocks is never smaller than the number of varieties. This is in fact the case for *every* BIBD, a result proved by R. A. Fisher in 1940. We omit the proof.

F. Yates (1902–1994)

Theorem 2.3: Fisher's inequality

In any balanced incomplete block design with v varieties and b blocks, $v \leq b$.

Problem 2.6

Use Fisher's inequality to show that in any balanced design the replication r and block size k satisfy the inequality $k \leq r$.

Problem 2.7

Give an example of each of the following:

(a)   a balanced design for which $v = b$;

(b)   a balanced design for which $v < b$.

R. A. Fisher (1890–1962)
Sir Ronald Fisher was statistician at Rothamsted Experimental Station from 1919-33 and thereafter professor at University College, London. He developed techniques for the analysis of variance and for the use and validation of small samples, and published his inequality in 1940. Frank Yates succeeded him at Rothamsted, where he later pioneered the use of computers in statistics.

Fisher's inequality shows that, in a balanced design with v varieties, the smallest possible number of blocks is v. Balanced designs for which $b = v$ have a special name.

> ### Definition
>
> A balanced incomplete block design is **symmetric** if $b = v$.

Recall that $vr = bk$ for any incomplete block design. Since $b = v$ for a symmetric design, it follows that $r = k$ for such designs. For example, design 1 is a symmetric design with $v = b = 7$ and $r = k = 3$.

It can be shown that the parameters of a symmetric design satisfy another condition. We state the result without proof.

> ### Theorem 2.4
>
> For a symmetric BIBD in which v is even, the number $r - \lambda$ must be the square of an integer.

Problem 2.8

Use Theorem 2.4, together with the condition $\lambda(v - 1) = r(k - 1)$, to show that there is no BIBD with $v = b = 22$ and $r = k = 7$.

We now look at the complements and the duals of balanced designs. It is natural to ask whether they are also BIBDs.

For complements, the situation is straightforward. In fact, the complement of *every* BIBD is balanced.

> ### Theorem 2.5
>
> Let Δ be a BIBD, and let $\overline{\Delta}$ be its complement. Then $\overline{\Delta}$ is also a BIBD.

Proof

Let Δ have parameters v, r, b, k and λ, and let A and B be any two varieties of $\overline{\Delta}$. These two varieties can occur together in $\overline{\Delta}$ only when the corresponding block of Δ contains neither of them.

In Δ there are r blocks containing A, and r blocks containing B. These include the λ blocks containing both A and B, and so the number of blocks containing neither A nor B is

$$b - (r - \lambda) - (r - \lambda) - \lambda = b - 2r + \lambda.$$

Thus the concurrence of A and B in $\overline{\Delta}$ is $b - 2r + \lambda$. This number is the same for all pairs of varieties, and so $\overline{\Delta}$ is balanced. ∎

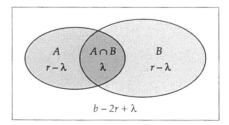

Theorem 2.5 is very useful in practice. For example, it is easier to search for balanced designs with small block sizes than with large ones. Thus, if we want to construct a BIBD with block size k, where k is greater than $v/2$, it is often easier to construct one with block size $v - k$ (which is less than $v/2$) and then take its complement. The following example illustrates this idea.

Example 2.2

Suppose that we wish to construct a BIBD with $v = 7$ and $k = 4$.

Since $k > v/2$, we look instead for a BIBD with $v = 7$ and $k = 7 - 4 = 3$. One such design is design 1. Taking its complement, we obtain a design with the given parameters:

1	2	3	4	5	6	7
A	B	C	D	E	F	G
B	C	D	E	F	G	A
D	E	F	G	A	B	C

design 1

1	2	3	4	5	6	7
C	A	A	A	B	A	B
E	D	B	B	C	C	D
F	F	E	C	D	D	E
G	G	G	F	G	E	F

complement of design 1

■

In the case of the dual, we can easily construct examples to show that the dual of a balanced design is not necessarily balanced. Such an example is provided by the following balanced design, whose dual you constructed in Problem 1.14.

1	2	3	4	5	6	7	8	9	10
A	B	C	D	E	A	B	C	D	E
B	C	D	E	A	C	D	E	A	B
F	F	F	F	F	D	E	A	B	C

Since the dual has 10 varieties and 6 blocks, Fisher's inequality is not satisfied, so the design is not balanced.

In fact, Fisher's inequality gives a necessary condition for the dual Δ^* of a BIBD Δ to be balanced. If Δ has v varieties and b blocks, then Δ^* has b varieties and v blocks, and so, applying Fisher's inequality to both Δ and Δ^*, we get $v \leq b$ and $b \leq v$; it follows that $b = v$. Thus, Δ^* can be balanced only when Δ is symmetric. It can be proved that this necessary condition is also sufficient, giving the following theorem. We omit the proof.

Theorem 2.6

Let Δ be a BIBD, and let Δ^* be its dual. Then Δ^* is a BIBD if and only if Δ is symmetric.

Problem 2.9

Design 1 is a balanced design. Verify that its dual is also balanced.

Problem 2.10

Prove that, if Δ is a symmetric BIBD, then Δ and Δ^* have the same concurrence λ.

We conclude this subsection with some general remarks on the role of balanced designs in the design of experiments. As there are many experiments in which all comparisons are of equal importance, we usually search for designs in which the concurrences are as equal as possible — balanced designs in the best case. But note that balanced designs are not *always* desirable.

In an experiment such as the fertilizer experiment (Example 1.5), the varieties are different combinations of various treatment factors, and the experimenters might reasonably expect the differences caused by each factor singly (the *main effects*) to be larger than those caused by the joint effect of the factors when their main effects have been allowed for (the *interactions*). In exploratory experiments, it is more important to estimate the main effects than the interactions. However, in later experiments, when the main effects are already approximately known, the experimenters might consider it more important to find out about the effect of the interactions. Being smaller, this effect needs more precision for it to be detected. In such situations, the experimenters may choose to sacrifice information on less important comparisons in order to gain more precision on important ones, and so they deliberately seek unequal concurrences.

Even when balance seems a desirable feature of a design, there may be overriding reasons why a balanced design should not be used. Fisher's inequality shows that the number of blocks in a BIBD is comparatively large, but in many experiments there are simply not that many blocks available. The experimenters usually have constraints of the following forms:

v (number of varieties)	—	already decided;
b (number of blocks)	—	an upper bound on the number available;
k (block size)	—	an upper bound, given by the smallest natural block, but preferably as large as possible within that bound;
r (replication)	—	a range of possibilities, bounded above by the amount of each variety available and by cost factors.

Within the range of possible parameters there may be no *balanced* design. Even if there is one, there may be no simple way for the experimenters to construct the required design, although they should certainly consult catalogues of BIBDs to see whether anyone has already done so.

2.3 Cyclic balanced designs

In a general incomplete block design the concurrence matrix may not have a very structured form. However, the following theorem shows that the concurrence matrix of a *cyclic* design does have a simple form: each row is obtained by shifting the previous row one place to the right, moving the last number round to the beginning.

In this subsection, the varieties are usually numbers, rather than letters. Once a design has been constructed, letters can then be substituted if desired.

Theorem 2.7

The rows of the concurrence matrix of a cyclic design are obtained by taking the first row and shifting it one, two, three, ... places to the right, each time moving the right-hand number back to the beginning.

For example, we have already seen that the concurrence matrix of design 1 (which is cyclic) has this property. Each row after the first row is obtained by shifting the previous row one place to the right.

$$\begin{bmatrix} 3 & 1 & 1 & 1 & 1 & 1 & 1 \\ 1 & 3 & 1 & 1 & 1 & 1 & 1 \\ 1 & 1 & 3 & 1 & 1 & 1 & 1 \\ 1 & 1 & 1 & 3 & 1 & 1 & 1 \\ 1 & 1 & 1 & 1 & 3 & 1 & 1 \\ 1 & 1 & 1 & 1 & 1 & 3 & 1 \\ 1 & 1 & 1 & 1 & 1 & 1 & 3 \end{bmatrix}$$

The reason that Theorem 2.7 holds is that, if i and j are any two varieties, and if i and j occur together in any block, then $i + 1$ and $j + 1$ occur together in the next block, $i + 2$ and $j + 2$ occur together in the next block, and so on.

In fact, we can say more. As we shall see, we can obtain the concurrence matrix of a cyclic design by examining a *single* block. The method uses modular arithmetic, which we summarize as follows.

Definition

Arithmetic modulo n is performed on the numbers $\{0, 1, 2, ..., n - 1\}$ by using ordinary arithmetic and then adding or subtracting an appropriate multiple of n to obtain a number in the set.

For example, for $n = 7$, we have

$$3 + 6 \, (= 9) = 2, \quad 3 - 6 \, (= -3) = 4, \quad 3 \times 6 \, (= 18) = 4.$$

Problem 2.11 ───────────────────────

Perform the following calculations modulo 11:

(a) $4 + 9$;   (b) $4 - 9$;   (c) 4×9.

The following example illustrates the method of determining the first row of a concurrence matrix.

Example 2.3

Consider the following design, which has seven varieties and starting block 0 1 2:

1	2	3	4	5	6	7
0	1	2	3	4	5	6
1	2	3	4	5	6	0
2	3	4	5	6	0	1

This design is isomorphic to design 2.

We construct a **table of differences** by writ[ing]
left and at the top of the table, as follows:

	0	1	2
0			
1			
2			

The entries in this table are obtained by subtracting each element at the top from each different element on the left, using arithmetic modulo 7.

For example, using the 2 on the left and the 1 at the top, we have $2 - 1 = 1$, and so 1 appears in the third row and second column; similarly, using the 0 on the left and the 2 at the top, we have $0 - 2 = 5$ (using arithmetic modulo 7), and so 5 appears in the first row and third column. Thus we can fill in two non-diagonal entries and the three diagonal entries.

	0	1	2
0	0		5
1		0	
2		1	0

Continuing in this way, we obtain the following table.

	0	1	2
0	0	6	5
1	1	0	6
2	2	1	0

The columns of this table correspond to the blocks that contain 0: 0 1 2, 6 0 1 and 5 6 0.

We can now construct the first row of the concurrence matrix. In each column we put the frequency of that column number in the above table; for example,

in column 0 we put **3**, since 0 occurs **3** times in the table;

in column 1 we put **2**, since 1 occurs **2** times in the table;

in column 5 we put **1**, since 5 occurs **1** time in the table;

in column 4 we put **0**, since 4 does not appear in the table.

The entry in column 0 is the replication r.

The first row of the concurrence matrix is therefore

columns	0	1	2	3	4	5	6
first row	3	2	1	0	0	1	2

Using Theorem 2.7, we now construct the concurrence matrix by successively shifting the rows one place to the right:

$$
\begin{array}{c}
\;\;0\;\;1\;\;2\;\;3\;\;4\;\;5\;\;6 \\
\begin{array}{c}0\\1\\2\\3\\4\\5\\6\end{array}
\left[
\begin{array}{ccccccc}
3 & 2 & 1 & 0 & 0 & 1 & 2 \\
2 & 3 & 2 & 1 & 0 & 0 & 1 \\
1 & 2 & 3 & 2 & 1 & 0 & 0 \\
0 & 1 & 2 & 3 & 2 & 1 & 0 \\
0 & 0 & 1 & 2 & 3 & 2 & 1 \\
1 & 0 & 0 & 1 & 2 & 3 & 2 \\
2 & 1 & 0 & 0 & 1 & 2 & 3
\end{array}
\right]
\end{array}
$$

The following theorem tells us that we can find the first row in this way for any cyclic design; the first row can always be obtained by counting the number of times each variety occurs in the table of differences.

Theorem 2.8

The first row of the concurrence matrix of a cyclic design is obtained by counting the number of times each variety occurs in the main body of the table of differences.

Problem 2.12

The following is a cyclic design with seven varieties and first block 0 1 3.

1	2	3	4	5	6	7
0	1	2	3	4	5	6
1	2	3	4	5	6	0
3	4	5	6	0	1	2

This design is isomorphic to design 1.

Use a table of differences to find the first row of the concurrence matrix for this design, and hence construct the concurrence matrix.

In solving Problem 2.12, you should have discovered that all the non-zero differences in the table occur the same number of times. This is always the case for a balanced design. The following theorem follows from Theorems 2.7 and 2.8.

Theorem 2.9

A cyclic design is balanced if and only if the first block has the property that all non-zero varieties occur equally often among its differences.

A first block which gives rise to equal frequencies for the differences is called a *perfect difference set*. The numbers in such a set may be thought of as points on a circle such that all distances between neighbouring points occur equally often.

Definition

A **perfect difference set** (modulo v) is a set of distinct numbers

$$\{b_1, b_2, \ldots, b_k\} \text{ (modulo } v)$$

such that the non-zero differences

$$b_1 - b_2, \ b_1 - b_3, \ \ldots, \ b_k - b_{k-1}$$

include each non-zero number (modulo v) equally often.

For example, $\{1, 2, 4\}$ is a perfect difference set (modulo 7). In the set of non-zero differences, each non-zero number (modulo 7), namely, 1, 2, 3, 4, 5, 6, occurs just once:

$$2 - 1 = 1, \quad 4 - 2 = 2, \quad 4 - 1 = 3,$$
$$1 - 2 = 6, \quad 2 - 4 = 5, \quad 1 - 4 = 4.$$

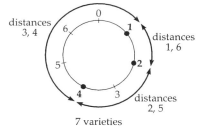

7 varieties

Problem 2.13

(a) By constructing the table of differences, show that $\{1, 3, 4, 5, 9\}$ is a perfect difference set (modulo 11).

(b) Use the result of part (a) to construct a cyclic BIBD with 11 varieties.

Problem 2.14

Which of the following are perfect difference sets (modulo 13)?

(a) $\{0, 1, 2, 3\}$;   (b) $\{0, 1, 4, 6\}$;   (c) $\{0, 1, 5, 7\}$.

It is one thing to recognize perfect difference sets; it is quite another to construct them. However, we can simplify the search a little by using the following observations.

- If one block of a cyclic design is a perfect difference set, then so is any other block.

For example, in the design in Problem 2.12, the blocks 0 1 3 and 1 2 4 are both perfect difference sets.

This means that we may choose a block that contains 0. Thus we may assume that the number 0 is contained in the set.

- If all concurrences are equal, and hence non-zero, then λ_{01} is non-zero, and so there is a block containing both 0 and 1.

This means that we may assume that the number 1 is contained in the set.

Apart from these simplifications, the construction is largely by trial and error, or by using more advanced theory.

In spite of these remarks, there is one theorem that we can use to obtain perfect difference sets. It uses the concept of a *non-zero square* (modulo v).

These numbers are obtained by writing down the squares 1^2, 2^2, 3^2, 4^2, ... and reducing the answers (modulo v).

For example, the non-zero squares (modulo 7) are

$$1^2 = 1; \quad 2^2 = 4; \quad 3^2(=9) = 2; \quad 4^2(=16) = 2; \quad 5^2(=25) = 4; \quad 6^2(=36) = 1;$$

thus, the non-zero squares are 1, 2 and 4 and the non-squares are 3, 5 and 6.

Note that we need to calculate only the squares of the numbers 1, 2, ..., $(v-1)/2$, since $(v-n)^2 = n^2$ (modulo v); for example, when $v = 7$, we need calculate only $1^2, 2^2$ and 3^2, since $4^2 = 3^2, 5^2 = 2^2$ and $6^2 = 1^2$. This cuts down the amount of work by half.

Problem 2.15

Write down:

(a) the non-zero squares (modulo 11);

(b) the non-zero squares (modulo 13).

We now state the theorem.

The proof uses finite fields, and is beyond the scope of this course.

Theorem 2.10

If v is a prime number of the form $4n + 3$, where n is a non-negative integer, then the set of non-zero squares (modulo v) is a perfect difference set.

Some prime numbers of the form $4n + 3$ are 3, 7, 11, 19, 23, 31, 43, ...

For example, for $v = 4 + 3 = 7$, the non-zero squares are 1, 2 and 4; it follows from Theorem 2.10 that {1, 2, 4} is a perfect difference set (modulo 7), as we have already seen.

Similarly, for $v = 8 + 3 = 11$, the non-zero squares are 1, 3, 4, 5 and 9, as you saw in Problem 2.15(a); it follows from Theorem 2.10 that {1, 3, 4, 5, 9} is a perfect difference set (modulo 11).

Problem 2.16

Write down the non-zero squares (modulo 19) and use them to write down a perfect difference set (modulo 19).

Constructions for BIBDs

We conclude this subsection with four general constructions for balanced designs, based on these ideas.

Construction 1

Let p be a prime number of the form $4n + 3$.

To obtain a symmetric balanced design with parameters

$$v = b = p, \quad r = k = (p-1)/2, \quad \lambda = (p-3)/4,$$

take as first block the set of non-zero squares (modulo p);
construct the other blocks using the cyclic construction.

For example, for $p = 11$, the non-zero squares are 1, 3, 4, 5 and 9, and we obtain the balanced design

See Problem 2.15(a).

1	2	3	4	5	6	7	8	9	10	11
1	2	3	4	5	6	7	8	9	10	0
3	4	5	6	7	8	9	10	0	1	2
4	5	6	7	8	9	10	0	1	2	3
5	6	7	8	9	10	0	1	2	3	4
9	10	0	1	2	3	4	5	6	7	8

Construction 2

Let p be a prime number of the form $4n + 1$.

To obtain a balanced design with parameters

$$v = p, \quad b = 2p, \quad r = p - 1, \quad k = (p-1)/2, \quad \lambda = (p-3)/2,$$

take the set of non-zero squares (modulo p), and the set of non-squares (modulo p), and use the cyclic construction in each case;

then put the two designs together.

Some prime numbers of the form $4n + 1$ are 5, 13, 17, 29, 37, 41, ...

For example, for $p = 5$, the non-zero squares are 1 and 4, the non-squares are 2 and 3, and we obtain the following design:

1	2	3	4	5	6	7	8	9	10
1	2	3	4	0	2	3	4	0	1
4	0	1	2	3	3	4	0	1	2

In this case the design is unreduced.

Construction 3

Let p be a prime number of the form $4n + 1$.

To obtain a balanced design with parameters

$$v = p + 1, \quad b = 2p, \quad r = p, \quad k = (p+1)/2, \quad \lambda = (p-1)/2,$$

take the set of squares (modulo p), including 0, and the set of non-zero squares (modulo p), together with an extra variety z, and use the cyclic construction in each case;

then put the two designs together.

We adopt the convention that z remains unchanged in the cyclic construction.

For example, for $p = 5$, the squares are 0, 1 and 4, the non-zero squares are 1 and 4, and we obtain the following design:

1	2	3	4	5	6	7	8	9	10
0	1	2	3	4	1	2	3	4	0
1	2	3	4	0	4	0	1	2	3
4	0	1	2	3	z	z	z	z	z

Construction 4

Let p be a prime number of the form $4n + 3$.

To obtain a balanced design with parameters

$$v = p + 1, \quad b = 2p, \quad r = p, \quad k = (p+1)/2, \quad \lambda = (p-1)/2,$$

take the set of non-zero squares (modulo p), together with an extra variety z, and the set of non-squares (modulo p), together with 0, and use the cyclic construction in each case;

then put the two designs together.

For example, for $p = 7$, the non-zero squares are 1, 2 and 4, the non-squares are 3, 5 and 6, and we obtain the following design:

1	2	3	4	5	6	7	8	9	10	11	12	13	14
1	2	3	4	5	6	0	0	1	2	3	4	5	6
2	3	4	5	6	0	1	3	4	5	6	0	1	2
4	5	6	0	1	2	3	5	6	0	1	2	3	4
z	z	z	z	z	z	z	6	0	1	2	3	4	5

Which of the above four constructions would you use to obtain BIBDs with the following sets of parameters?

(a) $v = 29$, $b = 58$, $r = 28$, $k = 14$, $\lambda = 13$;

(b) $v = 30$, $b = 58$, $r = 29$, $k = 15$, $\lambda = 14$;

(c) $v = 31$, $b = 31$, $r = 15$, $k = 15$, $\lambda = 7$;

(d) $v = 32$, $b = 62$, $r = 31$, $k = 16$, $\lambda = 15$.

2.4 Computer activities

The computer activities for this section are described in the *Computer Activities Booklet*.

After studying this section, you should be able to:

- explain the terms *concurrence matrix* and *concurrence* and construct the concurrence matrices of small designs;

- state and prove the equation $\lambda(v - 1) = r(k - 1)$;

- state Fisher's inequality, and theorems on the complement and dual of a BIBD;

- explain the term *symmetric design*;

- explain the term *perfect difference set*, and use such sets to construct cyclic balanced designs;

- use Constructions 1–4.

3 Special types of balanced design

In this section we describe three important types of balanced design. The first of these are the *Steiner triple systems*, which arise in various problems of recreational mathematics. The second are the *finite projective planes*, which we introduced in *Design 1*. Finally, we discuss *latin square* designs which are useful in particular circumstances.

Steiner triple systems, finite projective planes and latin squares are all of mathematical interest in their own right.

3.1 Steiner triple systems

Much of the early work on BIBDs centred around designs in which every block is small. When the block size k is 1, there are no connected designs, and when $k = 2$, the only connected BIBDs are unreduced designs in which the blocks are all possible pairs of varieties.

We disallow the trivial design with $v = 1$, because of the condition $k < v$.

The first interesting case occurs when $k = 3$. The smallest designs that can occur are those with $\lambda = 1$, and this leads to the following definition.

> **Definition**
>
> A **Steiner triple system** is a BIBD with $k = 3$ and $\lambda = 1$.

Problem 3.1

Use the conditions $\lambda(v-1) = r(k-1)$ and $vr = bk$ to show that, in any Steiner triple system,

(a) $r = (v-1)/2$;

(b) v is odd;

(c) $b = v(v-1)/6$.

Writing out the values of v for which v is odd and $v(v-1)/6$ is an integer, we get the sequence of numbers

$$7, 9, 13, 15, 19, 21, 25, \ldots,$$

each of which has the form $6n + 1$ or $6n + 3$, for some integer n.

Thus, in any Steiner triple system, v has the form $6n + 1$ or $6n + 3$ for some integer n.

This result is so important that we restate it as a theorem.

> ## Theorem 3.1
>
> In any Steiner triple system, v has the form $6n + 1$ or $6n + 3$ for some integer n.

It can be shown that Steiner triple systems exist for each of these values of v.

For $v = 7$, every Steiner triple system is isomorphic to design 1:

1	2	3	4	5	6	7
A	B	C	D	E	F	G
B	C	D	E	F	G	A
D	E	F	G	A	B	C

For $v = 9$, every Steiner triple system is isomorphic to

1	2	3	4	5	6	7	8	9	10	11	12
A	B	C	A	B	C	A	B	C	A	D	G
D	E	F	E	F	D	F	D	E	B	E	H
G	H	I	I	G	H	H	I	G	C	F	I

For all larger values of v of the form $6n + 1$ or $6n + 3$, there are many non-isomorphic Steiner triple systems; for example, for $v = 15$, there are 80 non-isomorphic Steiner triple systems. For larger values of v, the number of non-isomorphic Steiner triple systems is not known.

For $v = 13$, there are $(13 \times 12)/6 = 26$ blocks, by part (c) of Problem 3.1. The cyclic construction gives only 13 blocks, but we can put together two cyclic designs to obtain 26 blocks. We take the cyclic designs constructed from the blocks 0 1 4 and 0 5 7 respectively, and consider the design obtained by putting these designs together. In this design, variety 0 has concurrence 1 with every other variety. By the cyclic construction, all concurrences are 1, so this does provide a Steiner triple system with 13 varieties. The design is

1	2	3	...	12	13	14	15	16	...	25	26
0	1	2	...	11	12	0	1	2	...	11	12
1	2	3	...	12	0	5	6	7	...	3	4
4	5	6	...	2	3	7	8	9	...	5	6

We disallow the values $v = 1$ and $v = 3$, because of the condition $k < v$.

J. Steiner (1796–1863)
Jakob Steiner was a Swiss mathematician who spent most of his working life in Berlin. A pupil of the educational reformer Pestalozzi, he was an outstanding geometer who was a strong advocate of the synthetic approach to geometry.

For $v = 15$, there are $(15 \times 14)/6 = 35$ blocks, by part (c) of Problem 3.1. Interest in Steiner triple systems with fifteen varieties is largely due to the following problem, posed by the Reverend Thomas Kirkman in 1850.

---

15 schoolgirls problem

Is it possible for 15 schoolgirls to walk in 5 groups of 3 girls (so that each girl has two companions) on each of 7 successive days, in such a way that each girl is accompanied by every other girl exactly once?

Clearly, what is required is a Steiner triple system with 15 varieties, satisfying the extra condition that the blocks must be grouped together in fives to form the complete parties for each day. One solution to this puzzle is as follows:

Monday	*Tuesday*	*Wednesday*	*Thursday*
1 4 5 6 7	1 2 3 6 7	1 2 3 4 5	1 2 3 5 6
2 8 10 11 9	4 9 12 8 10	6 12 9 11 8	8 13 4 11 10
3 12 15 13 14	5 11 15 14 13	7 14 10 15 13	9 15 7 14 12

Friday	*Saturday*	*Sunday*
1 2 3 5 7	1 2 3 4 6	1 2 3 4 7
10 4 13 9 8	12 5 8 10 9	14 8 5 9 11
11 6 14 12 15	13 7 11 14 15	15 10 6 13 12

Problem 3.2

Find a solution to the corresponding '9 schoolgirls problem' — that of arranging walks for 9 schoolgirls in groups of 3 on 4 successive days, so that each girl is accompanied by every other girl exactly once.

Historical note

The development of Steiner triple systems was quite separate from that of experimental design. In 1853 Jakob Steiner described Steiner triple systems and showed that, for such a system, v must have the form $6n + 1$ or $6n + 3$ for some integer n. He asked whether every such value of v does in fact have a Steiner triple system, and in 1859 M. Reiss showed that this is indeed the case. Quite independently, and presumably unknown to Steiner and Reiss, Thomas Kirkman had asked and answered the same question in 1847. In 1850 Kirkman asked which of these designs can be split up into complete 'parties', as in the schoolgirls problem.

3.2   Finite projective planes

In *Design 1*, we introduced the following example.

Example 3.1:   the Fano plane

The **Fano plane** has seven points and seven lines, each line being incident with three points, and each point being incident with three lines. It can be drawn as follows.

Six of the lines are drawn as line segments, while one is drawn as a curve. In *Design 1* we labelled the points with numbers; here we use letters.

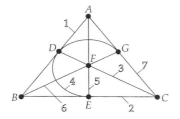

T. P. Kirkman (1806–1895) Thomas Penyngton Kirkman was rector of the parish of Croft in Lancashire for over fifty years. In his spare time he published a number of important papers in mathematics. He was elected a Fellow of the Royal Society in 1857.

The block table of the Fano plane lists the points that lie on each line, as follows:

1	2	3	4	5	6	7
A	B	C	D	E	F	G
B	C	D	E	F	G	A
D	E	F	G	A	B	C

This is design 1 of Section 2.

This block table is a cyclic block design with seven varieties arranged in seven blocks of size 3. ∎

We saw that the Fano plane is an example of a *finite projective plane*.

> ## Definition
>
> A **finite projective plane** is a regular incidence structure in which:
>
> (a) for each pair of distinct points, there is exactly one line incident with both;
>
> (b) for each pair of distinct lines, there is exactly one point incident with both.

The following example of a finite projective plane also appeared in *Design 1*.

Example 3.2: the 13-point plane

This projective plane has 13 points and 13 lines, each line being incident with four points, and each point being incident with four lines.

Again, we have labelled the points with letters.

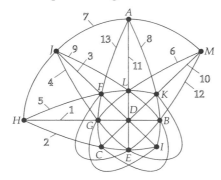

The block table of this projective plane is as follows:

1	2	3	4	5	6	7	8	9	10	11	12	13
B	C	D	E	F	G	H	I	J	K	L	M	A
D	E	F	G	H	I	J	K	L	M	A	B	C
G	H	I	J	K	L	M	A	B	C	D	E	F
H	I	J	K	L	M	A	B	C	D	E	F	G

This is a cyclic block design with thirteen varieties arranged in thirteen blocks of size 4. ∎

Each of these finite projective planes is a block design whose varieties correspond to the points and whose blocks correspond to the lines. Since any two points lie on just one line, any two varieties appear together in just one block; thus in each case we have a symmetric balanced design with $\lambda = 1$. The parameters of these block designs are as follows:

   7-point projective plane: $v = b = 7$, $r = k = 3$, $\lambda = 1$;

   13-point projective plane: $v = b = 13$, $r = k = 4$, $\lambda = 1$.

Any finite projective plane has equal numbers of points and lines, and these numbers are always of the form $n^2 + n + 1$, for some integer n. Moreover, there are exactly $n + 1$ points incident with each line and exactly $n + 1$ lines incident with each point.

In general, we make the following definition, which is equivalent to the definition given in *Design 1*. The 7-point and 13-point projective planes correspond to the cases $n = 2$ and $n = 3$, respectively.

It may seem more natural to take n points on each line and n lines through each point. The reason for taking $n + 1$ instead of n is given at the end of this subsection.

Definition

A **finite projective plane of order n** is a symmetric BIBD with the following parameters:

$$v = b = n^2 + n + 1, \quad r = k = n + 1, \quad \lambda = 1.$$

Problem 3.3

Verify the equation $\lambda(v - 1) = r(k - 1)$ for a finite projective plane of order n.

We now prove that these definitions are equivalent.

Theorem 3.2

The above two definitions of a projective plane are equivalent.

Proof

We first assume that Δ is a symmetric BIBD with parameters

$$v = b = n^2 + n + 1, \quad r = k = n + 1, \quad \lambda = 1.$$

We must prove that any two distinct points lie on just one line, and any two distinct lines pass through just one point.

We take the varieties of Δ as points and the blocks of Δ as lines; then the fact that $\lambda = 1$ implies that *any two points lie on just one line*.

Since Δ is a symmetric BIBD with $\lambda = 1$, its dual Δ^* is a symmetric BIBD with $\lambda^* = 1$, by Theorem 2.6 and Problem 2.10. But in Δ^* the varieties are the lines and the blocks are the points; thus, the fact that $\lambda^* = 1$ implies that *any two lines pass through just one point*.

We now assume that Δ is a regular incidence structure in which any two points lie on just one line and any two lines pass through just one point. We must prove that Δ is a symmetric BIBD with the given parameters.

We take the points of Δ as varieties and the lines of Δ as blocks. Since Δ is a regular incidence structure, we obtain a regular equi-replicate design. Thus, any two lines contain the same number of points and any two points pass through the same number of points. Moreover, since any two distinct points lie on exactly one line, this design is balanced with concurrence 1.

Suppose that the number of points on each line is $n + 1$. To show that the total number of points is $n^2 + n + 1$, we choose any point P and consider the lines passing through P. These lines are obtained by joining P to the $n + 1$ points on a given line l, as shown in the margin. Since each of these lines contains exactly n points other than P, the total number of points other than P is $n(n + 1)$, and so the total number of points including P is $n^2 + n + 1$, as required.

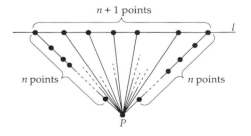

Thus we have a balanced design with $v = n^2 + n + 1$, $k = n + 1$ and $\lambda = 1$. Applying the equations $\lambda(v - 1) = r(k - 1)$ and $vr = bk$, we deduce that

$$r = \lambda(v - 1)/(k - 1) = 1 \times (n^2 + n)/n = n + 1,$$

and

$$b = vr/k = (n^2 + n + 1)(n + 1)/(n + 1) = n^2 + n + 1.$$

It follows that Δ is a symmetric BIBD with the required parameters. ∎

Projective planes of order n do not exist for all values of n. However, they do exist in the following important case.

Theorem 3.3

If n is a power of a prime number, then there exists a finite projective plane of order n.

We omit the proof of this theorem. Note that, by taking $n + 1$ as the number of points on each line, rather than n, we obtain an easy-to-state result; with n points on each line, we should have the less natural result that $n - 1$ is the power of a prime.

For example, there exist projective planes of order 2 (the Fano plane), 3 (the 13-point plane) and 4 (a projective plane with 21 points and 21 lines). However, there do not exist projective planes of order 6 or 10. It is not known whether there exist any projective planes of order n, when n is larger than 10 and not a prime power; for example, it is not known whether there exist projective planes of order 12, 15 or 18.

Problem 3.4 ————————————————————

Do there exist symmetric block designs with the following sets of parameters?

(a) $v = b = 91$, $r = k = 10$, $\lambda = 1$;

(b) $v = b = 111$, $r = k = 11$, $\lambda = 1$;

(c) $v = b = 133$, $r = k = 12$, $\lambda = 1$.

3.3 Latin square designs

Up to now we have concentrated mainly on designs for experiments with a *single* system of blocks, although we pointed out that in some situations the experimenter should make allowances for more than one type of block. In some situations there are two types of block which *cross* each other. The following example describes a typical situation.

Example 3.3

Consider an experiment designed to compare the effects of four drugs A, B, C, D in alleviating pain in sufferers from a chronic disease over a period of 2 years. In order to be sure of eliminating the effects of idiosyncratic reactions of individual patients, the doctor suggests that each patient should be given each drug in turn for a period of six months, say. If the disease is chronic, this is feasible. However, it is no good simply giving every patient drug A for the first six months, drug B for the second six months, and so on, since the severity of the disease may change with time. If the health of all the patients deteriorates during the experiment, then (whether or not this is a side-effect of drug A) the first and last drugs are not being tested in comparable conditions. So in this case *there are two types of block — patients* and *six month periods*. Each patient receives a single drug throughout each period, so the plots are the patient-months.

		months			
		1-6	7-12	13-18	19-24
	1				
patients	2				
	3				
	4				
	5				
	⋮				

How should the drugs be allocated? We have already specified that each patient should receive each drug for just one period, this eliminates differences between patients. To eliminate differences between time-periods, we should allocate each drug to a quarter of the patients in each period of six months.

If there were only four patients, a possible solution would be

		1-6	7-12	13-18	19-24
				months	
	1	A	B	C	D
patients	2	D	A	B	C
	3	C	D	A	B
	4	B	C	D	A

Typically there would be more than four patients in the experiment, but, provided the number of patients is a multiple of 4, we can simply use several copies of the above design. This design is an example of a *latin square*. ■

Definition

A **latin square of side** n is an $n \times n$ square with n symbols arranged in such a way that each symbol occurs just once in each row and just once in each column.

Examples of latin squares are:

A	B
B	A

and

1	2	3	4	5
2	4	5	3	1
3	1	4	5	2
4	5	2	1	3
5	3	1	2	4

Problem 3.5

(a) Construct a latin square of side 3 using the letters A, B and C.

(b) Complete the following latin squares:

1	–	3
–	–	2
–	3	–

(1)

A	–	B	–
–	–	D	–
–	B	–	–
–	–	–	C

(2)

Constructions for latin squares

There are a number of methods for constructing latin squares. Of these, the simplest are the *cyclic constructions* and the *Steiner triple system method.*

Cyclic construction

In the first row, write down n letters in any order.

In each subsequent row, shift the letters one place to the right, moving the last one to the beginning.

For example, for $n = 4$, the following latin square arises from this construction:

$$\begin{array}{cccc} A & B & C & D \\ D & A & B & C \\ C & D & A & B \\ B & C & D & A \end{array}$$

The following construction is a more general version of the cyclic construction.

Extended cyclic construction

In the first row, write down n letters in any order.

In each subsequent row, shift the letters r places to the right, moving the last r letters to the beginning; r can be any number from 1 to n such that r and n have no common factor.

If n is a prime number, then r can take any value from 2 to $n - 1$.

For example, for $n = 5$ and $r = 2$, the following latin square arises from this construction:

$$\begin{array}{ccccc} A & B & C & D & E \\ D & E & A & B & C \\ B & C & D & E & A \\ E & A & B & C & D \\ C & D & E & A & B \end{array}$$

Problem 3.6

(a) Use the extended cyclic construction with $n = 8$ and $r = 3$ to obtain a latin square with the symbols $A, B, ..., H$.

(b) Repeat part (a) with $r = 6$. What goes wrong?

The following construction is one of several constructions for latin squares using Steiner triple systems.

Steiner triple system construction

Take a Steiner triple system with n varieties labelled $0, 1, ..., n - 1$; label the rows and columns of the latin square similarly, and write $0, 1, ..., n - 1$ down the main diagonal.

The main diagonal goes from top left to bottom right.

For each pair of varieties A and B, find the block of the Steiner triple system containing the varieties A and B, and place the third variety of that block in row A and column B of the latin square.

For example, for $n = 7$, we take the Steiner triple system on the left below and construct the latin square on the right:

1	2	3	4	5	6	7
0	1	2	3	4	5	6
1	2	3	4	5	6	0
3	4	5	6	0	1	2

	0	1	2	3	4	5	6
0	0	–	–	–	–	–	–
1	–	1	–	–	–	–	–
2	–	–	2	–	–	–	–
3	–	–	–	3	–	–	–
4	–	–	–	–	4	–	–
5	–	–	–	–	–	5	–
6	–	–	–	–	–	–	6

Since variety 3 appears in the same block as varieties 0 and 1, we place 3 in row 0 and column 1 of the latin square; for the same reason, we can also place variety 3 in row 1 and column 0, variety 0 in row 1 and column 3 and in row 3 and column 1, and variety 1 in row 0 and column 3 and in row 3 and column 0. This gives the following pattern.

	0	1	2	3	4	5	6
0	0	3	–	1	–	–	–
1	3	1	–	0	–	–	–
2	–	–	2	–	–	–	–
3	1	0	–	3	–	–	–
4	–	–	–	–	4	–	–
5	–	–	–	–	–	5	–
6	–	–	–	–	–	–	6

Problem 3.7

Complete the above latin square using this construction.

Remarks on latin square designs

You may have noticed that the latin square solution to the design problem for the drug experiment works only because the blocks satisfy some special conditions:

* each type of block is *complete*, so we do not have the complication of constructing incomplete block designs for each family of blocks separately;

* each block of one type (patients) has exactly one plot in common with each block of the other type (six-month periods);

* in this case of just four patients, a typical block of each type has the same number of plots as there are varieties.

In spite of these conditions, the latin square is a very useful design. Before illustrating the wide applicability of latin squares, we consider another example.

There are various ways of adapting the basic latin square to less restrictive conditions, although we shall not deal with them in this course.

Example 3.4

Ten varieties of winter wheat are to be grown in a field consisting of one hundred plots laid out in a 10×10 array; each plot is a rectangle, not necessarily square. We have previously discussed the difficulty of deciding on the proper size and shape for blocks in this situation. One common solution is to adopt two families of blocks — the rows and the columns of the array. The reason behind this is that plots with similar fertility are likely to lie in neighbouring rows and columns, so that elimination of row differences and column differences will go a long way towards the elimination of genuine plot differences.

See Example 1.5.

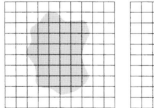
old waste tip

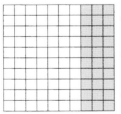
shade from trees

neighbouring plots have similar fertility

underground stream

neighbouring plots do not have similar fertility

In some situations this approach does not work — for example, fertility differences may correspond to diagonal lines. However, if there is no particular reason for suspecting this to be the case, then the experimenter is fairly safe in taking rows and columns as the two systems of blocks. If there are the same number of rows and columns, as in this example, then a latin square design is appropriate. A suitable latin square for this example can be constructed using the cyclic construction. ∎

Uses of latin squares

In spite of their apparent limitations, latin squares have many uses. In each of the uses described below we denote by n the size of one side of the square.

1. *Two systems each containing n complete blocks, each block of one system having just one plot in common with each block of the other system, and n varieties.*

This is the use we have described in the two preceding examples. In some applications, the layout of the plots may actually be square, as in the wheat experiment, but it does not need to be. In some applications, the blocks of one (or both) types may need to be placed in a particular order. For example, in the drug experiment, the time-periods occur in a definite order but the patients do not. In some experiments, there is no particular spatial or temporal ordering on either system of blocks.

2. *One system containing n blocks of size n, and n^2 varieties, which are all the possible combinations of two treatment factors, each of which has n different 'levels'.*

In this case the rows can be used for the blocks; the columns give the 'level' of the first factor; the letters give the 'level' of the second factor.

For example, consider an experiment to find the effect on tomato plants of four different types of watering schemes, labelled from 1 (for infrequent heavy watering) to 4 (for very frequent light watering) and four different types of compost, labelled A, B, C and D. There are four glasshouses, which form the blocks, and each of these has four plots — that is, groups of tomato plant receiving the same treatment. The varieties are the sixteen combinations such as $A1$, which denotes watering scheme 1 applied to plants grown in compost A. Using the latin square shown on the left, we obtain the design shown on the right:

Here there are the four 'levels' of watering and four 'levels' of compost treatment.

					1	2	3	4
A	B	C	D		A1	B1	C1	D1
D	A	B	C		D2	A2	B2	C2
C	D	A	B		C3	D3	A3	B3
B	C	D	A		B4	C4	D4	A4

The glasshouses are the blocks 1, 2, 3 and 4. The use of a latin square ensures that each glasshouse contains each compost and each watering scheme, even though no glasshouse is big enough to contain all sixteen varieties.

We introduce further uses of latin squares in Section 4.

After studying this section, you should be able to:

- explain the term *Steiner triple system*;
- state a result on the number of varieties of a Steiner triple system;
- explain the term *finite projective plane*, and give an example of one;
- write down the parameters of a finite projective plane of order n;
- state a result on the order of a finite projective plane;
- explain the term *latin square*;
- construct latin squares by applying various standard constructions;
- describe some uses for latin squares.

4 Resolvable designs

In the designs we have considered so far, we have always been concerned with the experiment as a whole. However, it is often desirable in practice to split an experiment into a number of smaller experiments. In this section we study the block designs that arise when this is possible.

4.1 Resolvability

In 1948 an experiment was carried out to compare sixteen allergens used to detect tuberculosis in cattle. It was decided that there were four main areas on each cow, each area being large enough for a complete test of about four of the allergens. In such circumstances it is natural to treat the areas as blocks and the individual cows as larger blocks. If between them the four blocks on each cow can have each allergen exactly once, then one can eliminate any variations between the responses of the cows to the allergens when estimating the differences between the allergens themselves.

There are several further reasons for wanting to split an experiment into smaller experiments.

Time   Certain operations to be carried out during an experiment take a long time, and external conditions may change during the process. For example, in a large cereal-growing experiment it may be impossible to harvest the whole crop in a single day. As it may rain overnight, there can be a substantial difference between plots that are harvested at different times. In order that the comparison of varieties is not affected by the different harvest times, the plots harvested on each day should include each variety equally often. Thus we need a design in which we can group the blocks into smaller equi-replicate designs.

Convenience   The technician with the job of running an experiment is rarely the person who devised it, and may be less interested in the intricacies of an elaborate design than in how to complete the job with the minimum of trouble. Thus, instructions such as 'water first this batch of blocks and then that batch' are more likely to be carried out correctly than complicated instructions such as 'first water the second plot in block 5, then ...'. Machines require this 'batching' of blocks just as much as people do: for example, modern farm machinery makes it impracticable to plough, seed, hoe or spray a small area of land at a time.

Extra treatments   It is not uncommon for an experimenter to introduce a new treatment once an experiment is already under way. For example, in an experiment on fruit, designed to compare different root-stocks, the experimenter may also decide to see whether spraying the fruit has any effect. A treatment such as spraying is conveniently applied only to whole blocks at a time. In order that the effects of the spraying do not become muddled with those of the differences between root-stocks, the sprayed blocks should include each variety equally often.

Averting disaster   Sometimes something may go wrong with part of an experiment — for example, crows may eat most of the corn in one of the fields. If the experiment is laid out so that it divides into groups of blocks containing each variety just once, then it is more likely that the undamaged part of the experiment will include all varieties equally often, and so give as precise information as is possible under the circumstances.

We make the following definitions.

Definitions

A **replicate** is a set of plots containing each variety exactly once.

An incomplete block design is **resolvable** if its blocks can be grouped into replicates.

For example, the design

1	2	3	4	5	6	7	8	9	10	11	12
A	A	A	A	B	B	B	C	C	C	D	G
B	D	E	F	D	E	F	D	E	F	E	H
C	G	I	H	I	H	G	H	G	I	F	I

is resolvable as its blocks can be grouped into four replicates as follows:

2	6	10	3	7	8	4	5	9	1	11	12
A	B	C	A	B	C	A	B	C	A	D	G
D	E	F	E	F	D	F	D	E	B	E	H
G	H	I	I	G	H	H	I	G	C	F	I

This design is essentially the Steiner triple system with 9 varieties given in the solution to Problem 3.2.

Similarly, the design given in the solution to Kirkman's '15 schoolgirls problem' in Section 3 is resolvable. Indeed, the requirement that the blocks of schoolgirls can be grouped into complete parties for the various days is exactly the condition of resolvability.

Problem 4.1

Decide whether each the following designs is resolvable. For each resolvable design, group the blocks into replicates.

(a)

1	2	3	4	5	6	7	8
A	B	A	B	A	B	C	A
C	C	B	D	D	C	D	D
F	F	E	E	F	E	F	E

(b)

1	2	3	4	5	6
A	B	C	D	E	F
C	D	A	C	B	B
F	E	F	E	A	D

While attempting Problem 4.1, you may have noticed that, for each resolvable design, the number of varieties must be divisible by the block size. We now prove that this is always the case.

Notation

We denote by s the number of blocks in each replicate in a resolvable design.

The letter s is in standard use for this parameter.

Theorem 4.1

In a resolvable incomplete block design,

(a) $v = sk$; (b) $b = rs$.

Theorem 4.1 shows that a design cannot be resolvable unless v/k is an integer.

Proof

(a) In each replicate there are s blocks of size k, making sk plots altogether. Each variety occurs just once in each replicate, so there are v plots in a replicate. Thus $v = sk$.

(b) Each variety occurs once in each replicate and r times altogether, so there are r replicates. Each replicate contains s blocks, so there are rs blocks altogether. Thus $b = rs$. ∎

Problem 4.2

For which values of v can there exist resolvable Steiner triple systems with v varieties?

There are few designs that are both resolvable and balanced, because a resolvable balanced design needs even more blocks than an arbitrary balanced design. The following result is an extended version of Fisher's inequality. We omit the proof.

Theorem 4.2

In any resolvable BIBD, $b \geq v + r - 1$.

An example of a design that is both balanced and resolvable is the Steiner triple system with nine varieties; here, $v = 9$, $b = 12$ and $r = 4$, and so $b = v + r - 1$ in this case.

Problem 4.3

Verify the inequality in Theorem 4.2 for a Steiner triple system with 15 varieties.

4.2 Constructions for resolvable designs

In many practical situations the number of plots is extremely limited, and so the parameters b and r must be small. This means that, on average, the concurrences must also be small. In Section 2 we showed that when all the concurrences are the same their common value is equal to $r(k-1)/(v-1)$. Even if the concurrences are not the same, their average value must be $r(k-1)/(v-1)$. This is approximately equal to rk/v, which equals r/s, by Theorem 4.1. But in many situations, r is so small that $r/s < 1$; this means that the average concurrence is less than 1, so that some concurrences must be 0. For the same average concurrence, we obtain a more even spread when each concurrence is 0 or 1 than when some concurrences are 0 while others have value 2 or more.

In view of this, we make the following definition.

Definition

A **(0, 1)-design** is a block design in which each concurrence is 0 or 1.

The rest of this section is devoted to some important constructions for resolvable (0, 1)-designs.

Square lattice designs

In 1936 Frank Yates introduced a family of resolvable (0, 1)-designs called *square lattice designs*. They are very simple to construct and, of all the resolvable designs with the same parameters, they have been shown to be the most 'efficient' designs in terms of the overall precision of their estimates. They apply when $s = k$, so that $v = k^2$ is a perfect square. The construction is as follows.

Construction of simple lattice design

Write down the k^2 varieties in any order in a $k \times k$ square array.

For the first replicate, take the *rows* of the square as blocks of the design.

For the second replicate, take the *columns* of the square as blocks of the design.

For example, for $v = 16$ and $k = 4$, we proceed as follows.

We first label the varieties 1 – 16, and write them in a 4 × 4 square array in any order, such as

1	2	3	4
5	6	7	8
9	10	11	12
13	14	15	16

The blocks of the first replicate are the rows of this square array:

1	2	3	4
1	5	9	13
2	6	10	14
3	7	11	15
4	8	12	16

The blocks of the second replicate are the columns of the array:

5	6	7	8
1	2	3	4
5	6	7	8
9	10	11	12
13	14	15	16

These two replicates are the minimum that we need to obtain a *connected* design, and the resulting 2-replicate design is called a **simple lattice design**. Note that any two varieties in the same row occur together in the first replicate but not in the second, and any two varieties in the same column occur together in the second replicate but not in the first. No other pairs of varieties occur together. Thus the simple lattice designs are (0, 1)-designs.

We can extend the above construction, without destroying the (0, 1)-property, to obtain a 3-replicate design, called a **triple lattice design**, as follows.

Construction of triple lattice design

Construct a simple lattice design with two replicates as above.

Construct a third replicate from the square array as follows.

The first block contains all varieties on the main (top-left to bottom-right) diagonal. The other blocks are the other 'diagonals' in the same direction.

For example, for $v = 16$, the top-left to bottom-right diagonals are

```
1 ↘ 2 ↘ 3 ↘ 4 ↘
5 ↘ 6 ↘ 7 ↘ 8 ↘
9 ↘ 10 ↘ 11 ↘ 12 ↘
13   14   15   16
```

and the blocks of the third replicate are

9	10	11	12
1	2	3	4
6	7	8	5
11	12	9	10
16	13	14	15

Combining these replicates, we obtain the following design:

1	2	3	4		5	6	7	8		9	10	11	12
1	5	9	13		1	2	3	4		1	2	3	4
2	6	10	14		5	6	7	8		6	7	8	5
3	7	11	15		9	10	11	12		11	12	9	10
4	8	12	16		13	14	15	16		16	13	14	15
	replicate 1					replicate 2					replicate 3		

Note that any two varieties which occur together in the third replicate do not appear in the same row or column, and so they do not occur together in either of the first two replicates. Thus we have a (0, 1)-design.

Problem 4.4 ───────────────────────────────

Construct a 3-replicate square lattice design with 25 varieties (labelled $A, B, ..., Y$) in blocks of size 5.

Rectangular lattice designs

An obvious disadvantage of the square lattice construction is that it applies only when the number of varieties is a perfect square. In 1947 B. Harshbarger extended the above idea to cover the case when $s = k + 1$ and $v = k(k + 1)$. The construction is as follows.

Construction of rectangular lattice design

Write down the $k(k + 1)$ varieties in any order in a $(k + 1) \times (k + 1)$ square array with the main diagonal missing.

For the first replicate, take the *rows* of the square as blocks of the design.

For the second replicate, take the *columns* of the square as blocks of the design.

For example, for $v = 12$ and $k = 3$, we proceed as follows.

We label the varieties $1 - 12$, and write them in a 4×4 square array in any order, such as

–	1	2	3
4	–	5	6
7	8	–	9
10	11	12	–

The blocks of the first replicate are the rows of this square array:

						–	1	2	3
1	2	3	4			4	–	5	6
1	4	7	10			7	8	–	9
2	5	8	11			10	11	12	–
3	6	9	12				square array		

The blocks of the second replicate are the columns of the array:

5	6	7	8
4	1	2	3
7	8	5	6
10	11	12	9

Combining these replicates, we obtain the following design:

1	2	3	4	5	6	7	8
1	4	7	10	4	1	2	3
2	5	8	11	7	8	5	6
3	6	9	12	10	11	12	9
	replicate 1				replicate 2		

In general, we cannot go on to construct a third replicate in the way we did for square lattice designs.

Problem 4.5

Construct a 2-replicate rectangular lattice design with 20 varieties $A, B, ..., T$, in blocks of size 4.

By omitting further diagonals, we can extend the rectangular lattice construction to any situation in which $k < s$. For example, we can obtain a 2-replicate rectangular lattice design with 15 varieties in blocks of size 3 by noting that $v = 15$, $k = 3$, and so $s = 5$. Since $s - k = 2$, we omit *two* diagonals from a 5×5 square array, as follows:

–	–	1	2	3
4	–	–	5	6
7	8	–	–	9
10	11	12	–	–
–	13	14	15	–

The resulting 2-replicate design is

1	2	3	4	5	6	7	8	9	10
1	4	7	10	13	4	8	1	2	3
2	5	8	11	14	7	11	12	5	6
3	6	9	12	15	10	13	14	15	9
		replicate 1					replicate 2		

Problem 4.6

Construct a 2-replicate rectangular lattice design with 8 varieties (1, 2, 3, ... 8) in blocks of size 2. Do this in two ways:

(a) by omitting neighbouring diagonals of the appropriate square;

(b) by omitting alternate diagonals.

Compare the two designs.

The previous problem illustrates the fact that, when $s - k > 1$, different choices of the diagonals to be removed can lead to essentially different designs. The effect is not always as drastic as that we have just seen: omitting the 'wrong' diagonals does not necessarily lead to a disconnected design, but it can give a design whose overall precision is less than it need be. Thus rectangular lattices should be used with great care when $s - k > 1$. Although you can eliminate the disconnected designs yourself, you would be wise to seek a statistician's advice as to the relative merits of the various possible connected designs.

4.3 Orthogonal latin squares and resolvability

Latin squares are of widespread use in the design of experiments. We now illustrate their use in the construction of resolvable designs.

Recall from Section 4.2 that we can use the square lattice design to obtain a 3-replicate (0, 1)-design, provided that the number of varieties is a perfect square. To do this, we start with a square array of numbers and take its rows as the blocks of the first replicate, its columns as the blocks of the second replicate, and its diagonals as the blocks of the third replicate; for example, for 16 varieties, we obtain the following design:

1	2	3	4		5	6	7	8		9	10	11	12				
1	5	9	13		1	2	3	4		1	2	3	4		1	2	3	4
2	6	10	14		5	6	7	8		6	7	8	5		5	6	7	8
3	7	11	15		9	10	11	12		11	12	9	10		9	10	11	12
4	8	12	16		13	14	15	16		16	13	14	15		13	14	15	16

replicate 1   replicate 2   replicate 3   square array

Another way of obtaining the third replicate is to take the latin square given below and note the positions of each letter in relation to the square array, as follows:

A	B	C	D
D	A	B	C
C	D	A	B
B	C	D	A

letter A appears in positions 1, 6, 11 and 16, so we take these numbers as the varieties in block 9;

letter B appears in positions 2, 7, 12 and 13, so we take these numbers as the varieties in block 10;

letter C appears in positions 3, 8, 9 and 14, so we take these numbers as the varieties in block 11;

letter D appears in positions 4, 5, 10 and 15, so we take these numbers as the varieties in block 12.

So far, nothing has been gained by using latin squares. We now show how we can use latin squares to obtain more than three replicates. The method uses the concept of *orthogonal latin squares*. To understand this idea, consider the following two latin squares:

A	B	C	D		A	B	C	D
B	A	D	C		C	D	A	B
C	D	A	B		D	C	B	A
D	C	B	A		B	A	D	C

latin square 1   latin square 2

We now superimpose these two latin squares into a 4 × 4 square array of ordered pairs of letters so that, in each pair:

the first letter is the corresponding letter in the first latin square;
the second letter is the corresponding letter in the second latin square;

for example, the pair *DB* in the bottom left-hand corner arises from the letters *D* and *B* in the bottom left-hand corners of the separate latin squares.

The phrase *ordered pair* means that, for example, the pair *DB* is regarded as different from the pair *BD*.

AA	BB	CC	DD
BC	AD	DA	CB
CD	DC	AB	BA
DB	CA	BD	AC

Note that each of the sixteen possible ordered pairs of letters *AA*, *AB*, *AC*, ..., *DD* occurs just once; when this happens, the latin squares are said to be *orthogonal*.

Definition

Two $n \times n$ latin squares are **orthogonal** if, when they are superimposed, each of the n^2 possible ordered pairs of letters occurs just once.

We now use the above two orthogonal latin squares to obtain further replicates for the square lattice design. Recall that the first two replicates, derived from the rows and columns of the square array, are as follows:

1	2	3	4		5	6	7	8
1	5	9	13		1	2	3	4
2	6	10	14		5	6	7	8
3	7	11	15		9	10	11	12
4	8	12	16		13	14	15	16

replicate 1   replicate 2

1	2	3	4
5	6	7	8
9	10	11	12
13	14	15	16

square array

To obtain two more replicates, we consider the orthogonal latin squares above and note the positions of each letter in turn, as follows:

We no longer use the diagonals of the square array, because there is no latin square orthogonal to the one we considered previously. (See Exercise 4.5.)

Third replicate

letter *A* appears in positions 1, 6, 11 and 16, so we take these numbers as the varieties in block 9;
letter *B* appears in positions 2, 5, 12 and 15, so we take these numbers as the varieties in block 10;
letter *C* appears in positions 3, 8, 9 and 14, so we take these numbers as the varieties in block 11;
letter *D* appears in positions 4, 7, 10 and 13, so we take these numbers as the varieties in block 12.

9	10	11	12
1	2	3	4
6	5	8	7
11	12	9	10
16	15	14	13

replicate 3

A	B	C	D
B	A	D	C
C	D	A	B
D	C	B	A

latin square 1

Fourth replicate

letter *A* appears in positions 1, 7, 12 and 14, so we take these numbers as the varieties in block 13;
letter *B* appears in positions 2, 8, 11 and 13, so we take these numbers as the varieties in block 14;
letter *C* appears in positions 3, 5, 10 and 16, so we take these numbers as the varieties in block 15;
letter *D* appears in positions 4, 6, 9 and 15, so we take these numbers as the varieties in block 16.

13	14	15	16
1	2	3	4
7	8	5	6
12	11	10	9
14	13	16	15

replicate 4

A	B	C	D
C	D	A	B
D	C	B	A
B	A	D	C

latin square 2

Collecting the replicates together, we obtain the following 4-replicate (0, 1)-design:

1	2	3	4	5	6	7	8	9	10	11	12	13	14	15	16
1	5	9	13	1	2	3	4	1	2	3	4	1	2	3	4
2	6	10	14	5	6	7	8	6	5	8	7	7	8	5	6
3	7	11	15	9	10	11	12	11	12	9	10	12	11	10	9
4	8	12	16	13	14	15	16	16	15	14	13	14	13	16	15

replicate 1	replicate 2	replicate 3	replicate 4

Problem 4.7

(a) Construct a 4×4 latin square with first row $A\ B\ C\ D$ which is orthogonal to each of the above orthogonal latin squares.

   Hint   Which letter must appear in the bottom-left corner?

(b) Use the latin square in part (a) to construct a fifth replicate for the above (0, 1)-design.

4.4   Computer activities

The computer activities for this section are described in the *Computer Activities Booklet*.

After studying this section, you should be able to:

- explain the terms *resolvable design, replicate* and (0,1)-*design*;
- appreciate the importance of resolvable designs in the design of experiments;
- construct 2-replicate and 3-replicate square lattice designs;
- construct 2-replicate rectangular lattice designs;
- recognize orthogonal latin squares and use them to construct resolvable (0,1)-designs.

---

5   Balanced designs and codes

In *Design 3* we gave several examples of error-detecting and error-correcting codes, and we introduced the idea of *Hamming distance*. In particular, we showed that

- if the minimum Hamming distance is δ, and if δ is odd, then the code can detect and correct up to $(\delta - 1)/2$ errors.

Design 3, Theorem 1.1

- if the minimum Hamming distance is δ, and if δ is even, then the code can detect up to $\delta/2$ errors and correct up to $(\delta - 2)/2$ errors.

It follows that the more 'spread out' the codewords are, the more errors the code can detect and correct.

It is natural to ask whether we can construct codes in which all the Hamming distances between pairs of codewords are approximately the same, and thus are well spread out. In this section we show that we can do better than this. Starting with a balanced block design, we show how its incidence matrix gives rise to a binary code in which *all the Hamming distances are equal*.

5.1 Codes derived from BIBDs

Before describing the method in general, we look at a particular example.

Example 5.1

Consider the following BIBD with parameters $v = 6$, $b = 10$, $r = 5$, $k = 3$ and $\lambda = 2$:

1	2	3	4	5	6	7	8	9	10
A	B	C	D	E	A	B	C	D	E
B	C	D	E	A	C	D	E	A	B
F	F	F	F	F	D	E	A	B	C

The incidence matrix of this design is the following 6×10 matrix $\mathbf{B}$:

$$
\begin{array}{c}
A \\ B \\ C \\ D \\ E \\ F
\end{array}
\begin{bmatrix}
1 & 0 & 0 & 0 & 1 & 1 & 0 & 1 & 1 & 0 \\
1 & 1 & 0 & 0 & 0 & 0 & 1 & 0 & 1 & 1 \\
0 & 1 & 1 & 0 & 0 & 1 & 0 & 1 & 0 & 1 \\
0 & 0 & 1 & 1 & 0 & 1 & 1 & 0 & 1 & 0 \\
0 & 0 & 0 & 1 & 1 & 0 & 1 & 1 & 0 & 1 \\
1 & 1 & 1 & 1 & 1 & 0 & 0 & 0 & 0 & 0
\end{bmatrix}
$$

Let us now consider the code whose codewords are the *rows* of this matrix. Since $v = 6$ and $b = 10$, we have six codewords of length 10:

1000110110, 1100001011, 0110010101, 0011011010, 0001101101, 1111100000.

If we compare any two of these codewords, we find that the Hamming distance between them is 6. For example, if we compare the first two codewords, we get

```
1  0  0  0  1  1  0  1  1  0
1  1  0  0  0  0  1  0  1  1
   ↑        ↑  ↑  ↑  ↑     ↑
```

It follows that this code detects up to three errors and corrects up to two errors. ∎

We can apply the method of this example to any balanced design. If Δ is a BIBD with parameters v, b, r, k and λ, then $\mathbf{B}$, the incidence matrix of Δ, is a $v \times b$ matrix. Taking the rows of $\mathbf{B}$ as codewords, we obtain a code with v codewords, each of length b.

If we compare any two of these codewords, we find that the number 1 occurs together in exactly λ positions in both codewords, since the concurrence λ is the number of times any two varieties occur together in the same block. In Example 5.1, the numbers 1 and 1 coincide in exactly two positions in any two codewords, since $\lambda = 2$; for example,

```
1  0  0  0  1  1  0  1  1  0
1  1  0  0  0  0  1  0  1  1
↑                 ↑
```

Also, since there are exactly r 1s in each codeword, there must be

> $r - \lambda$ positions for which 1 occurs in the first codeword and 0 occurs in the second,

and

> $r - \lambda$ positions for which 0 occurs in the first codeword and 1 occurs in the second.

In Example 5.1, we have $r - \lambda = 3$, and so there are three positions for which 1 occurs in the first codeword and 0 occurs in the second, and three positions for which 0 occurs in the first codeword and 1 occurs in the second; for example:

$$\quad\quad\quad \downarrow \;\; \downarrow \quad\quad\; \downarrow$$
$$1\;\; 0\;\; 0\;\; 0\;\; 1\;\; 1\;\; 0\;\; 1\;\; 1\;\; 0$$
$$1\;\; 1\;\; 0\;\; 0\;\; 0\;\; 0\;\; 1\;\; 0\;\; 1\;\; 1$$
$$\uparrow \quad\quad\quad\quad\quad \uparrow \quad\quad\; \uparrow$$

Finally, since there are b positions altogether, the positions where 0 occurs in both codewords must be

$b - \lambda - (r - \lambda) - (r - \lambda)$ (that is, $b - 2r + \lambda$).

In Example 5.1, the numbers 0 and 0 coincide exactly twice in any two codewords, since

$b - 2r + \lambda = 10 - (2 \times 5) + 2 = 2;$

for example:

$$1\;\; 0\;\; 0\;\; 0\;\; 1\;\; 1\;\; 0\;\; 1\;\; 1\;\; 0$$
$$1\;\; 1\;\; 0\;\; 0\;\; 0\;\; 0\;\; 1\;\; 0\;\; 1\;\; 1$$
$$\quad\;\; \uparrow \;\; \uparrow$$

If we reorder the positions to make the pattern clearer, we can summarize the above arrangements diagrammatically, as follows:

$1 \ldots 1$	$1 \ldots 1$	$0 \ldots 0$	$0 \ldots 0$
$1 \ldots 1$	$0 \ldots 0$	$1 \ldots 1$	$0 \ldots 0$
λ	$r - \lambda$	$r - \lambda$	$b - 2r + \lambda$

Thus we have established the following theorem.

Theorem 5.1

Let Δ be a BIBD with v varieties, b blocks, replication r, block-size k, and concurrence λ. Let C be the code whose codewords are the rows of the incidence matrix. Then the Hamming distance between any two codewords is $2(r - \lambda)$, and the code C detects up to $r - \lambda$ errors and corrects up to $r - \lambda - 1$ errors.

Problem 5.1

For each of the following BIBDs, write down:

(a) the values of v, b, r, k and λ;

(b) the codewords corresponding to the rows of the incidence matrix;

(c) the constant Hamming distance between each pair of these codewords;

(d) the number of errors detected and corrected by the corresponding code.

1	2	3	4	5	6	7
A	B	C	D	E	F	G
B	C	D	E	F	G	A
D	E	F	G	A	B	C

design 1

1	2	3	4	5	6	7	8	9	10	11	12
A	B	C	A	B	C	A	B	C	A	D	G
D	E	F	E	F	D	F	D	E	B	E	H
G	H	I	I	G	H	H	I	G	C	F	I

design 3

It follows from the above discussion that, whenever we have a BIBD, we can construct a corresponding code, and this suggests that we look back at Sections 2 and 3 for examples of BIBDs and consider their corresponding codes. For example, we can obtain a class of codes from the Steiner triple systems.

Recall that a Steiner triple system is a BIBD with $k = 3$ and $\lambda = 1$. It follows from the equations $\lambda(v-1) = r(k-1)$ and $vr = bk$ that

$$r = (v-1)/2 \quad \text{and} \quad b = v(v-1)/6,$$

We obtained these results in Problem 3.1.

and that v has the form $6n + 1$ or $6n + 3$, for some integer n.

Using the above construction, we obtain a code from each Steiner triple system; any code of this type is called a **Steiner code**. Such a code has v codewords of length $v(v-1)/6$, and the Hamming distance between any two codewords is $2(r-\lambda)$, which is $v-3$. This code therefore detects up to $(v-3)/2$ errors and corrects up to $(v-5)/2$ errors.

In Problem 5.1, you constructed Steiner codes corresponding to $v = 7$ and $v = 9$.

Problem 5.2

Earlier we described some BIBDs with the following sets of parameters:

(a) $v = b = p$, where p is a prime number of the form $4n + 3$,

    $r = k = (p-1)/2, \quad \lambda = (p-3)/4;$

See Construction 1 in Section 2.3.

(b) $v = p$, where p is a prime number of the form $4n + 1$,

    $b = 2p, \quad r = p-1, \quad k = (p-1)/2, \quad \lambda = (p-3)/2;$

See Construction 2 in Section 2.3.

In each case, find the Hamming distance between any two codewords, and write down the number of errors detected and corrected by the corresponding code.

Problem 5.3

Using the results of Problem 5.2, explain how you would construct:

(a) a code with 17 codewords of length 34 and Hamming distance 18;

(b) a code with 19 codewords of length 19 and Hamming distance 10.

In each case, write down the number of errors detected and corrected by such a code.

After studying this section, you should be able to:

•   explain how to construct a code from a balanced design;

•   determine the Hamming distance of such a code.

Further reading

The following books are recommended for reference.

W. G. Cochran and G. B. Cox, *Experimental Designs* (2nd edition), Wiley, 1957 (paperback reprint 1992).

D. R. Cox, *Planning of Experiments,* Wiley, 1958 (reprinted 1964).

O. L. Davies, *Design and Analysis of Industrial Experiments* (2nd edition), Longman group, 1979 (reprinted with corrections).

D. J. Finney, *An Introduction to the Theory of Experimental Design,* University of Chicago Press, 1960.

R. A. Fisher, *Statistical Methods, Experimental Design, and Scientific Inference,* Oxford University Press, 1990.

R. A. Fisher and F. Yates, *Statistical Tables for Biological, Agricultural and Medical Research* (6th edition), Longman, 1974.

J. Dénes and A. D. Keedwell, *Latin Squares and their Applications,* English Universities Press, 1974.

Most of these books are concerned with the statistical aspects of the design and analysis of experiments and are not primarily concerned with design as such. R. A. Fisher's two books are classic statistical texts on experimental design. The book by D. R. Cox contains no mathematics, but gives much clear and helpful advice to scientists on planning experiments. The book by Cochran and Cox contains information on the design of experiments, but is mainly concerned with the analysis of variance technique for analysing the results of experiments. The *Tables* by Fisher and Yates give some orthogonal latin squares and a list of BIBDs, as do the plans in Cochran and Cox; Davies also includes a list of BIBDs. A thorough treatment of latin squares, together with a full bibliography, is given in Dénes and Keedwell.

The following books are more mathematical.

P. J. Cameron and J. H. van Lint, *Designs, Graphs, Codes and their Links*, London Mathematical Society, Student Texts **22**, 1991.

J. H. van Lint and R. M. Wilson, *A Course in Combinatorics*, Cambridge University Press, 1992.

V. Bryant, *Aspects of Combinatorics*, Cambridge University Press, 1993.

Exercises

Section 1

1.1 Are the following designs connected? Are they equi-replicate?

(a)

1	2	3	4
1	2	3	4
3	4	1	5
5	3	2	1

(b)

1	2	3	4	5	6
A	C	G	E	D	I
G	D	B	F	H	B
E	H	A	I	C	F

1.2 Draw the bipartite graph associated with the following design:

1	2	3	4	5	6
A	B	E	C	D	C
D	F	A	F	B	E

1.3 We can associate a block design with a graph by labelling all the vertices and edges. The edges correspond to blocks and the vertices to varieties; each block contains two varieties — its vertices. Write down the block design corresponding to each of the following graphs.

For other ways of associating a block design with a graph, see *Design 1*, Problem 5.1 and Exercise 5.2.

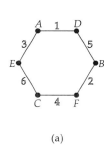

(a)

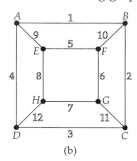

(b)

1.4

(a) Using the circle construction, write down a design with
$$v = b = 8, r = k = 3.$$

(b) Using the cyclic construction, write down a design with
$$v = b = 8, r = k = 3.$$

1.5 Which of the following cyclic designs is connected?

(a) $v = 12, k = 3$, first block 0 6 8;

(b) $v = 12, k = 3$, first block 2 8 5;

(c) $v = 13, k = 3$, first block 0 3 6.

1.6 Construct:

(a) the cyclic design with $v = 7, k = 4$, and first block 0 1 2 5;

(b) the complement of the design in part (a);

(c) the dual of the design in part (a).

Section 2

2.1 Consider the following cyclic design:

1	2	3	4	5
0	1	2	3	4
2	3	4	0	1
3	4	0	1	2

(a) By examining the blocks containing variety 0, write down the replication, the concurrences λ_{01}, λ_{02}, λ_{03} and λ_{04}, and the first row of the concurrence matrix. Use Theorem 2.7 to construct the concurrence matrix $\mathbf{C}$.

(b) Write down the incidence matrix $\mathbf{B}$ of this design, and use it to calculate the concurrence matrix $\mathbf{C} = \mathbf{B}\mathbf{B}^T$.

   Verify that your answer agrees with that of part (a).

(c) Write down the table of differences for the block 0 2 3 (modulo 5), and use Theorem 2.8 to find the first row of the concurrence matrix.

   Verify that your answer agrees with those of parts (a) and (b).

2.2 The following numbers are the parameters of BIBDs. Use the equations $vr = bk$ and $\lambda(v - 1) = r(k - 1)$ to fill in the missing numbers.

(a) $v = 9$, $b = ?$, $r = 4$, $k = 3$, $\lambda = ?$;

(b) $v = ?$, $b = 12$, $r = 8$, $k = ?$, $\cdot \lambda = 5$;

(c) $v = ?$, $b = 13$, $r = ?$, $k = 4$, $\lambda = 1$.

2.3 Explain why there are no BIBDs with the following sets of parameters:

(a) $v = 10$, $b = 16$, $r = 8$, $k = 5$, $\lambda = 3$;

(b) $v = 45$, $b = 15$, $r = 4$, $k = 12$, $\lambda = 1$;

(c) $v = 46$, $b = 46$, $r = 10$, $k = 10$, $\lambda = 2$.

2.4 A cyclic design is required for six varieties in blocks of size 3. As remarked in Section 2.3, we may assume that the first block contains 0 and 1, and so is 0 1 2, 0 1 3, 0 1 4 or 0 1 5. In each case, write down the table of differences, and hence determine which first blocks give the smallest spread of concurrences.

2.5

(a) By constructing a table of differences, determine whether {2, 3, 5, 11} is a perfect difference set (modulo 13).

(b) Try to construct a perfect difference set of three numbers (modulo 5). Why is this impossible?

(c) For which numbers $k = 2, 3, 4, 5$ or 6 do there exist perfect difference sets of size k (modulo 7)?

2.6

(a) Construct a BIBD with 13 varieties arranged in 26 blocks of size 6.
   Hint   Use the result of Problem 2.15(b).

(b) Construct a symmetric BIBD with 19 varieties arranged in 19 blocks of size 9.
   Hint   Use the result of Problem 2.16.

2.7 Which of the four constructions would you use to construct a balanced design with each of the following sets of parameters:

(a) $v = 59, \quad b = 59, \quad r = 29, \quad k = 29, \quad \lambda = 14$;

(b) $v = 60, \quad b = 118, \quad r = 59, \quad k = 30, \quad \lambda = 29$;

(c) $v = 61, \quad b = 122, \quad r = 60, \quad k = 30, \quad \lambda = 29$;

(d) $v = 62, \quad b = 122, \quad r = 61, \quad k = 31, \quad \lambda = 30$.

2.8 How would you construct a symmetric BIBD with v varieties and block-size $v - 1$? Determine the value of λ for such a design.

2.9

(a) A BIBD is *self-complementary* if it is isomorphic to its complement.

Show that such a design must have an even number of varieties and blocks, and write down a self-complementary BIBD with 4 varieties and 6 blocks.
Hint Use the results of Problem 1.13.

(b) A BIBD is *self-dual* if it is isomorphic to its dual.

Show that such a design must be symmetric, and write down a self-dual BIBD with 7 varieties.
Hint Use the results of Problem 1.15.

2.10 Let Δ be a balanced design with parameters v, b, r, k and λ. Using techniques of linear algebra, it can be proved that the determinant of the incidence matrix **B** of Δ satisfies the equation

$$(\det \mathbf{B})^2 = rk(r - \lambda)^{v-1}.$$

Use this result to prove Theorem 2.4.

Section 3

3.1 For each integer n, consider the design obtained by taking as varieties the $2^n - 1$ n-digit binary words (other than 00 ... 0) and as blocks any pair of these words together with the word obtained by adding the corresponding digits (modulo 2).

For example, for $n = 3$, the block containing the varieties 1 1 0 and 0 1 1 also contains their sum 1 0 1.

(a) Show that the resulting design is a Steiner triple system, and determine its parameters in terms of n.

(b) Which Steiner triple systems correspond to the cases $n = 3$ and $n = 4$?

3.2 An *affine plane of order n* is a BIBD obtained by taking a projective plane of order n, removing any one block, and deleting the varieties in that block wherever they occur.

(a) Show that the resulting design has parameters

$$v = n^2, \quad b = n^2 + n, \quad r = n + 1, \quad k = n, \quad \lambda = 1.$$

(b) Construct affine planes of orders 2 and 3.

3.3 Complete, if possible, the following latin squares:

(a)

A	–	–	D
–	–	–	–
–	–	–	B
–	D	C	–

(b)

B	–	A	–
–	–	–	–
–	B	–	D
A	–	–	–

(c)

–	–	D	–	B
–	A	–	E	–
–	–	–	D	–
–	E	–	–	–
–	–	C	–	–

Section 4

4.1 Decide whether the following designs are resolvable; if so, group the blocks into replicates.

(a)

1	2	3	4	5	6
A	B	A	B	C	A
C	C	B	D	D	D
F	F	E	E	F	E

(b)

1	2	3	4	5	6
A	B	C	D	E	F
C	D	A	C	B	B
F	E	F	E	A	D

4.2 Explain how you would construct:

(a) a 2-replicate resolvable (0, 1)-design for 42 varieties in blocks of size 6;

(b) a 3-replicate resolvable (0, 1)-design for 36 varieties in blocks of size 6.

4.3 Explain why every affine plane is resolvable.

An affine plane is defined in Exercise 3.2.

4.4 Are the following latin squares orthogonal?

A	B	C	D	E		A	B	C	D	E
E	A	B	C	D		D	E	A	B	C
D	E	A	B	C		B	C	D	E	A
C	D	E	A	B		E	A	B	C	D
B	C	D	E	A		C	D	E	A	B

4.5 Does there exist a latin square orthogonal to the following latin square?

A	B	C	D
D	A	B	C
C	D	A	B
B	C	D	A

Section 5

5.1 How many errors are detected and corrected by the code arising from

(a) the projective plane of order n?

(b) the affine plane of order n (defined in Exercise 3.2)?

5.2 Using the results of Exercise 5.1, explain how you would construct

(a) a code with 21 codewords of length 21 and Hamming distance 8;

(b) a code with 16 codewords of length 20 and Hamming distance 8.

Solutions to the exercises

1.1

(a) This design is connected, since each variety can be compared directly or indirectly with every other variety; it is not equi-replicate since, for example, variety 1 appears three times, whereas variety 2 occurs twice.

(b) This design is not connected, since the varieties C, D and H cannot be compared, either directly or indirectly, with the other varieties; it is equi-replicate with $r = 2$.

1.2

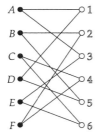

1.3

(a)

1	2	3	4	5	6
A	B	A	C	B	C
D	F	E	F	D	E

(b)

1	2	3	4	5	6	7	8	9	10	11	12
A	B	C	A	E	F	G	E	A	B	C	D
B	C	D	D	F	G	H	H	E	F	G	H

1.4

(a)

1	2	3	4	5	6	7	8
A	D	G	B	E	H	C	F
B	E	H	C	F	A	D	G
C	F	A	D	G	B	E	H

(b) We can choose any block as the first block; choosing $A\,B\,C$, we obtain the design

1	2	3	4	5	6	7	8
A	B	C	D	E	F	G	H
B	C	D	E	F	G	H	A
C	D	E	F	G	H	A	B

1.5

(a) This design is not connected, since blocks 1, 3, 5, 7, 9 and 11 contain . only the varieties 0, 2, 4, 6, 8 and 10, and the remaining blocks contain only the varieties 1, 3, 5, 7, 9 and 11.

(b) This design is not connected, since blocks 1, 4, 7 and 10 contain only the varieties 2, 5, 8 and 11, blocks 2, 5, 8 and 11 contain only the varieties 0, 3, 6 and 9, and the remaining blocks contain only the varieties 1, 4, 7 and 10.

(c) This design is connected.

1.6

(a)

1	2	3	4	5	6	7
0	1	2	3	4	5	6
1	2	3	4	5	6	0
2	3	4	5	6	0	1
5	6	0	1	2	3	4

(b) The complement of the design in part (a) is:

1	2	3	4	5	6	7
3	4	5	6	0	1	2
4	5	6	0	1	2	3
6	0	1	2	3	4	5

(c) The dual of the design in part (a) is:

0	1	2	3	4	5	6
1	2	3	4	5	6	7
3	4	5	6	7	1	2
6	7	1	2	3	4	5
7	1	2	3	4	5	6

2.1

(a) By inspection,

$$\lambda_{01} = 1, \ \lambda_{02} = 2, \ \lambda_{03} = 2, \ \lambda_{04} = 1.$$

Since $r = 3$, the first row of the concurrence matrix is

3 1 2 2 1.

By Theorem 2.7, the concurrence matrix is

$$\begin{bmatrix} 3 & 1 & 2 & 2 & 1 \\ 1 & 3 & 1 & 2 & 2 \\ 2 & 1 & 3 & 1 & 2 \\ 2 & 2 & 1 & 3 & 1 \\ 1 & 2 & 2 & 1 & 3 \end{bmatrix}$$

(b)

$$\mathbf{B} = \begin{array}{c} \\ 0 \\ 1 \\ 2 \\ 3 \\ 4 \end{array} \begin{array}{c} \begin{matrix} 1 & 2 & 3 & 4 & 5 \end{matrix} \\ \begin{bmatrix} 1 & 0 & 1 & 1 & 0 \\ 0 & 1 & 0 & 1 & 1 \\ 1 & 0 & 1 & 0 & 1 \\ 1 & 1 & 0 & 1 & 0 \\ 0 & 1 & 1 & 0 & 1 \end{bmatrix} \end{array}$$

$$\mathbf{BB}^T = \begin{bmatrix} 1 & 0 & 1 & 1 & 0 \\ 0 & 1 & 0 & 1 & 1 \\ 1 & 0 & 1 & 0 & 1 \\ 1 & 1 & 0 & 1 & 0 \\ 0 & 1 & 1 & 0 & 1 \end{bmatrix} \begin{bmatrix} 1 & 0 & 1 & 1 & 0 \\ 0 & 1 & 0 & 1 & 1 \\ 1 & 0 & 1 & 0 & 1 \\ 1 & 1 & 0 & 1 & 0 \\ 0 & 1 & 1 & 0 & 1 \end{bmatrix} = \begin{bmatrix} 3 & 1 & 2 & 2 & 1 \\ 1 & 3 & 1 & 2 & 2 \\ 2 & 1 & 3 & 1 & 2 \\ 2 & 2 & 1 & 3 & 1 \\ 1 & 2 & 2 & 1 & 3 \end{bmatrix} = \mathbf{C}$$

which agrees with part (a).

(c) Working modulo 5, we obtain the table of differences

	0	2	3
0	0	3	2
2	2	0	4
3	3	1	0

The number of times that the varieties 0, 1, 2, 3, 4 occur in this table are, respectively,

3 1 2 2 1.

By Theorem 2.8, this gives the first row of the concurrence matrix. This agrees with the answers in parts (a) and (b).

2.2

(a) $b = 12$, $\lambda = 1$;

(b) We have
$$v8 = 12k \quad \text{and} \quad 5(v-1) = 8(k-1).$$
Substituting $v = 3k/2$ into the second equation, we obtain
$$15k/2 = 8k - 3.$$
Hence $k = 6$ and $v = 9$.

(c) We have
$$vr = 13 \times 4 \quad \text{and} \quad v - 1 = r3.$$
Substituting $r = (v-1)/3$ into the first equation, we obtain
$$v(v-1) = 13 \times 12.$$
Hence $v = 13$ and $r = 4$.

2.3

(a) For such a design, $\lambda(v-1) \neq r(k-1)$, contradicting Theorem 2.2.

(b) For such a design, $v > b$, contradicting Fisher's inequality (Theorem 2.3).

(c) For such a symmetric design, v is even, but $r - \lambda = 8$, which is not the square of an integer, contradicting Theorem 2.4.

2.4 Working modulo 6, we obtain the tables of differences

	0	1	2
0	0	5	4
1	1	0	5
2	2	1	0

	0	1	3
0	0	5	3
1	1	0	4
3	3	2	0

	0	1	4
0	0	5	2
1	1	0	3
4	4	3	0

	0	1	5
0	0	5	1
1	1	0	2
5	5	4	0

The first rows of the concurrence matrices are therefore

3 2 1 0 1 2, 3 1 1 2 1 1, 3 1 1 2 1 1, 3 2 1 0 1 2,

respectively. It follows that the first blocks that give the most nearly equal spread of concurrences are 0 1 3 and 0 1 4.

2.5

(a) Working modulo 13, we obtain the table of differences

	2	3	5	11
2	0	12	10	4
3	1	0	11	5
5	3	2	0	7
11	9	8	6	0

Since each non-zero number 1, 2, ... , 12 appears exactly once in this table, the set {2, 3, 5, 11} is a perfect difference set (modulo 13).

(b) If we start with a set of three numbers, the table of differences must have the following form:

	*	*	*
*	0	*	*
*	*	0	*
*	*	*	0

But it is impossible for the six non-zero differences to include the four numbers 1, 2, 3, 4 equally often. Thus no such perfect difference set exists.

(c) Since the $k(k-1)$ non-zero differences must include the six numbers 1, 2, ..., 6 equally often, 6 must divide $k(k-1)$. This rules out $k = 2$ and $k = 5$. For $k = 3, 4$ and 6, we have the perfect difference sets

$$\{0, 1, 5\}, \quad \{0, 1, 2, 4\}, \quad \{0, 1, 2, 3, 4, 5\},$$

respectively.

2.6

(a) We use Construction 2 with $p = 13$. We obtain a cyclic BIBD by taking as first blocks the non-zero squares {1, 3, 4, 9, 10, 12} and the non-squares {2, 5, 6, 7, 8, 11}, as follows:

The non-zero squares (modulo 13) were obtained in Problem 2.15(b).

1	2	3	4	5	6	7	8	9	10	11	12	13
1	2	3	4	5	6	7	8	9	10	11	12	0
3	4	5	6	7	8	9	10	11	12	0	1	2
4	5	6	7	8	9	10	11	12	0	1	2	3
9	10	11	12	0	1	2	3	4	5	6	7	8
10	11	12	0	1	2	3	4	5	6	7	8	9
12	0	1	2	3	4	5	6	7	8	9	10	11

14	15	16	17	18	19	20	21	22	23	24	25	26
2	3	4	5	6	7	8	9	10	11	12	0	1
5	6	7	8	9	10	11	12	0	1	2	3	4
6	7	8	9	10	11	12	0	1	2	3	4	5
7	8	9	10	11	12	0	1	2	3	4	5	6
8	9	10	11	12	0	1	2	3	4	5	6	7
11	12	0	1	2	3	4	5	6	7	8	9	10

(b) We use Construction 1 with $p = 19$. We obtain a cyclic BIBD by taking the perfect difference set in Problem 2.16 as its first block, as follows:

1	2	3	4	5	6	7	8	9	10	11	12	13	14	15	16	17	18	19
1	2	3	4	5	6	7	8	9	10	11	12	13	14	15	16	17	18	0
4	5	6	7	8	9	10	11	12	13	14	15	16	17	18	0	1	2	3
5	6	7	8	9	10	11	12	13	14	15	16	17	18	0	1	2	3	4
6	7	8	9	10	11	12	13	14	15	16	17	18	0	1	2	3	4	5
7	8	9	10	11	12	13	14	15	16	17	18	0	1	2	3	4	5	6
9	10	11	12	13	14	15	16	17	18	0	1	2	3	4	5	6	7	8
11	12	13	14	15	16	17	18	0	1	2	3	4	5	6	7	8	9	10
16	17	18	0	1	2	3	4	5	6	7	8	9	10	11	12	13	14	15
17	18	0	1	2	3	4	5	6	7	8	9	10	11	12	13	14	15	16

2.7

(a) Use construction 1 with $p = 59$;

(b) use construction 4 with $p = 59$;

(c) use construction 2 with $p = 61$;

(d) use construction 3 with $p = 61$.

2.8 Use the all-combinations method of Section 1.4 with $k = v - 1$. Each block is obtained by taking all but one of the varieties, omitting a different variety each time. Such a design is balanced, with

$$\lambda = r(k-1)/(v-1) = (v-1)(v-2)/(v-1) = v-2.$$

2.9

(a) By the results of Problem 1.13, we have

$$k = v - k \quad \text{and} \quad r = b - r.$$

Thus $v = 2k$ and $b = 2r$, and so v and b are both even.

A self-complementary BIBD with 4 varieties and 6 blocks is

1	2	3	4	5	6
A	A	A	B	B	C
B	C	D	C	D	D

(b) By the results of Problem 1.15, we have $v = b$, so the design must be symmetric.

A self-dual BIBD with 7 varieties and 7 blocks is

1	2	3	4	5	6	7
A	B	C	D	E	F	G
B	C	D	E	F	G	A
D	E	F	G	A	B	C

This is design 1 of Section 2.1.

2.10 Consider a symmetric design for which v is even. For a symmetric design, $v = b$ so $r = k$, and so

$$(\det \mathbf{B})^2 = r^2(r-\lambda)^{v-1}.$$

Since r^2 and $(\det \mathbf{B})^2$ are both perfect squares, and $v - 1$ is odd,

$$r - \lambda \text{ must also be a perfect square.}$$

3.1

(a) The design has $v = 2^n - 1$ varieties and block-size $k = 3$. Since any two varieties uniquely determine the third variety in the block, each pair of varieties occur together in just one block. Thus the design is balanced with $\lambda = 1$. It follows that

$$r = \lambda(v-1)/(k-1) = 1 \times (2^n - 2)/2 = 2^{n-1} - 1,$$

and

$$b = vr/k = (2^n - 1)(2^{n-1} - 1)/3.$$

(b) For $n = 3$, we obtain the Steiner triple system with 7 varieties (design 1) in the following form:

1	2	3	4	5	6	7
001	010	100	011	110	111	101
010	100	011	110	111	101	001
011	110	111	101	001	010	100

For $n = 4$, we obtain a Steiner triple system with 15 varieties and 35 blocks. It is isomorphic to the Kirkman '15 schoolgirls puzzle' design in Section 3.1.

3.2

(a) An affine plane of order n clearly has $n^2 + n$ blocks. Since we have deleted $n + 1$ varieties, the number of varieties is

$$v = (n^2 + n + 1) - (n + 1) = n^2.$$

Each of the remaining varieties still occurs $n + 1$ times, and so $r = n + 1$.

Since the projective plane is a balanced design with $\lambda = 1$, each pair of remaining varieties occur together just once, and so an affine plane is also a BIBD with $\lambda = 1$.

The block size k can be calculated either from $vr = bk$ or from $\lambda(v - 1) = r(k - 1)$, giving $k = n$.

(b) Removing the last block and the corresponding varieties from the 7-point and 13-point projective planes in Section 3.2, we obtain the following affine planes:

$n = 2$:

1	2	3	4	5	6
B	B	D	D	E	F
D	E	F	E	F	B

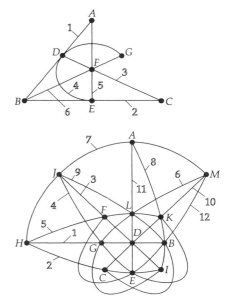

$n = 3$:

1	2	3	4	5	6	7	8	9	10	11	12
B	E	D	E	H	I	H	I	J	K	L	M
D	H	I	J	K	L	J	K	L	M	D	B
H	I	J	K	L	M	M	B	B	D	E	E

3.3

(a)

A	C	B	D
D	B	A	C
C	A	D	B
B	D	C	A

(b) no such latin square exists

(c)

E	C	D	A	B
D	A	B	E	C
C	B	E	D	A
B	E	A	C	D
A	D	C	B	E

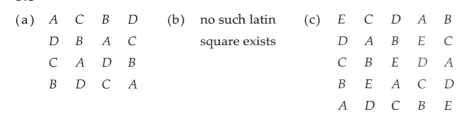

4.1

(a) This design is resolvable; its replicates are:

1, 4; 2, 6; 3, 5.

(b) This design is not resolvable.

4.2

(a) Use the rectangular lattice design construction: start with a 7×7 array with the main diagonal missing, and write down the rows and columns of this array.

(b) Use the square lattice design construction: start with a 6×6 array, and write down its rows, columns and diagonals.

4.3 Each affine plane arises by taking a finite projective plane, removing a block (line) $v_1, v_2, \ldots, v_k$, and deleting the varieties (points) in that block wherever they occur. The resulting design is always resolvable: the replicates correspond to

the blocks (lines) that originally contained v_1;

the blocks (lines) that originally contained v_2;

. . .

the blocks (lines) that originally contained v_k.

For example, for the 9-point affine plane in Exercise 3.2, we obtain the replicates:

for variety B: $A\,I\,K$, $C\,J\,L$, $D\,G\,H$;

for variety E: $A\,D\,L$, $C\,H\,I$, $G\,J\,K$;

for variety F: $A\,C\,G$, $D\,I\,J$, $H\,K\,L$;

for variety M: $A\,H\,J$, $C\,D\,K$, $G\,I\,L$,

4.4 Yes — on superimposing them we obtain

AA	BB	CC	DD	EE
ED	AE	BA	CB	DC
DB	EC	AD	BE	CA
CE	DA	EB	AC	BD
BC	CD	DE	EA	AB

which contains each possible pair of letters just once.

4.5 No. Suppose that there exists a latin square orthogonal to the given one. We can assume without loss of generality that its first row is $A\,B\,C\,D$. Its second row is then either $C\,D\,A\,B$ or $B\,C\,D\,A$. In the former case, it is impossible to complete the first column; in the latter case it is impossible to complete the first two columns. Thus no such latin square exists.

5.1

(a) The Hamming distance is

$$2(r - \lambda) = 2\{(n + 1) - 1\} = 2n,$$

so the code detects up to n errors and corrects up to $n - 1$ errors.

(b) The values of r and λ are the same as in part (a) (see Exercise 3.2), and so the code detects up to n errors and corrects up to $n - 1$ errors.

5.2

(a) Take the design in Exercise 5.1(a) with $n = 4$;

the code detects up to 4 errors and corrects up to 3 errors.

(b) Take the code in Exercise 5.1(b) with $n = 4$;

the code detects up to 4 errors and corrects up to 3 errors.

Solutions to the problems

Solution 1.1

(a) $v = 5, b = 4, k = 3$;

(b) $v = 9, b = 6, k = 3$.

Solution 1.2

Block design (a) is not equi-replicate; varieties 1 and 3 occur three times each, whereas varieties 2, 4 and 5 occur just twice.

Block design (b) is equi-replicate; each variety occurs twice, so $r = 2$.

Solution 1.3

(a) The parameters are $v = 9, r = 2, b = 6, k = 3$;
     thus $vr = 9 \times 2 = 18$ and $bk = 6 \times 3 = 18$, and so $vr = bk$.

(b) The parameters are $v = 7, r = 3, b = 7, k = 3$;
     thus $vr = 7 \times 3 = 21$ and $bk = 7 \times 3 = 21$, and so $vr = bk$.

Solution 1.4

There are many possible solutions — for example, relabel the varieties and blocks as follows:

$$0 \to Y, \quad 1 \to E, \quad 2 \to W, \quad 3 \to A, \quad 4 \to T, \quad 5 \to R, \quad 6 \to H.$$
$$\mathbb{A} \to 1, \quad \mathbb{B} \to 6, \quad \mathbb{C} \to 5, \quad \mathbb{D} \to 7, \quad \mathbb{E} \to 3, \quad \mathbb{F} \to 4, \quad \mathbb{G} \to 2.$$

Solution 1.5

(a) Varieties F and H are directly comparable, as they both appear in block 7.

(b) Varieties C and G are neither directly nor indirectly comparable.

(c) Varieties A and E are not directly comparable, but they are indirectly comparable as A is directly comparable with variety D (in block 4) and D is directly comparable with variety E (in block 6).

Solution 1.6

There are many possible solutions — for example:

1	2	3	4	5	6	7	8
A	B	C	D	E	F	G	H
B	C	D	E	F	G	H	A

Solution 1.7

The associated bipartite graphs are

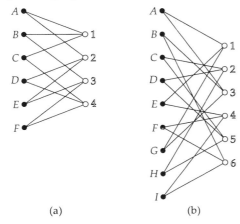

(a)   (b)

Graph (a) is connected, so design (a) is connected.
Graph (b) is not connected, so design (b) is not connected.

For example, in graph (b) there is no path from vertex B to vertex C.

Solution 1.8

(a)

	1	2	3	4	5	6
A	1	0	1	0	0	0
B	0	0	1	0	0	1
C	0	1	0	0	1	0
D	0	1	0	0	1	0
E	1	0	0	1	0	0
F	0	0	0	1	0	1
G	1	0	1	0	0	0
H	0	1	0	0	1	0
I	0	0	0	1	0	1

(b)

	A	B	C	D	E	F	G
A	1	0	0	0	1	0	1
B	1	1	0	0	0	1	0
C	0	1	1	0	0	0	1
D	1	0	1	1	0	0	0
E	0	1	0	1	1	0	0
F	0	0	1	0	1	1	0
G	0	0	0	1	0	1	1

Notice that this incidence matrix is the transpose of the incidence matrix of the design in Example 1.7, given on page 12.

Solution 1.9

(a) We obtain the following design with $\binom{5}{2} = 10$ blocks:

1	2	3	4	5	6	7	8	9	10
A	A	A	A	B	B	B	C	C	D
B	C	D	E	C	D	E	D	E	E

(b) We obtain the following design with $\binom{5}{3} = 10$ blocks:

1	2	3	4	5	6	7	8	9	10
A	A	A	A	A	A	B	B	B	C
B	B	B	C	C	D	C	C	D	D
C	D	E	D	E	E	D	E	E	E

Solution 1.10

1	2	3	4	5	6
A	E	C	A	E	C
B	F	D	B	F	D
C	A	E	C	A	E
D	B	F	D	B	F

The design is connected.

Solution 1.11

(a)

1	2	3	4	5	6	7
0	1	2	3	4	5	6
1	2	3	4	5	6	0
3	4	5	6	0	1	2

The design is connected.

(b)

1	2	3	4	5	6
1	2	3	4	5	0
3	4	5	0	1	2
5	0	1	2	3	4

The design is not connected.

(c)

1	2	3	4	5	6
A	B	C	D	E	F
C	D	E	F	A	B
D	E	F	A	B	C
F	A	B	C	D	E

The design is connected.

Solution 1.12

1	2	3	4	5
3	0	0	1	1
4	2	4	3	2

Solution 1.13

Each block of $\overline{\Delta}$ corresponds to a block of Δ, and so $\overline{b} = b$.

Since each block of Δ has k varieties and there are v varieties altogether, each block of $\overline{\Delta}$ has $v - k$ varieties, and so $\overline{k} = v - k$.

If a given variety occurs in a block of Δ, then it does not occur in the corresponding block of $\overline{\Delta}$; thus each variety occurs $b - r$ times, and so $\overline{r} = b - r$.

Since each variety in Δ occurs $b - r$ times in $\overline{\Delta}$, the number of varieties is unchanged, and so $\overline{v} = v$.

We have

$$\overline{v}\,\overline{r} = v\,(b-r) = v\,b - v\,r = v\,b - b\,k = b(v-k) = \overline{b}\,\overline{k},$$

so the parameters $\overline{v}$, $\overline{r}$, $\overline{b}$ and $\overline{k}$ satisfy Theorem 1.1.

Note that no varieties can be lost on taking complements, because if $b = r$, then $v = k$, by Theorem 1.1, contradicting the fact that $k < v$.

Solution 1.14

A	B	C	D	E	F
1	1	2	3	4	1
5	2	3	4	5	2
6	7	6	6	7	3
8	9	8	7	8	4
9	10	10	9	10	5

Solution 1.15

The blocks of Δ^* correspond to the varieties of Δ and the varieties of Δ^* correspond to the blocks of Δ, and so $b^* = v$ and $v^* = b$.

In the bipartite graph of the design Δ, the degree of each variety-vertex is r and the degree of each block-vertex is k. But each variety-vertex in the bipartite graph of Δ corresponds to a block-vertex of Δ^*, and each block-vertex in the bipartite graph of Δ corresponds to a variety-vertex of Δ^*, and so $r = k^*$ and $k = r^*$.

We have

$$v^*r^* = bk = vr = b^*k^*,$$

so the parameters v^*, r^*, b^* and k^* satisfy Theorem 1.1.

Solution 2.1

For design 1 we have:

(a) 1;   (b) 1;   (c) 1.

For design 2 we have:

(a) 2;   (b) 1;   (c) 0.

Thus design 1 seems to be a better design to use if we wish to compare varieties the same number of times.

Solution 2.2

(a) This design is not a balanced design since, for example, $\lambda_{AB} = 1$ but $\lambda_{AC} = 0$.

(b) This design is a balanced design with $\lambda = 2$.

Solution 2.3

The concurrence matrix is

$$
\begin{array}{c c}
 & \begin{array}{cccccc} A & B & C & D & E & F \end{array} \\
\begin{array}{c} A \\ B \\ C \\ D \\ E \\ F \end{array} &
\left[\begin{array}{cccccc}
2 & 1 & 1 & 1 & 1 & 0 \\
1 & 2 & 1 & 0 & 1 & 1 \\
1 & 1 & 2 & 1 & 0 & 1 \\
1 & 0 & 1 & 2 & 1 & 1 \\
1 & 1 & 0 & 1 & 2 & 1 \\
0 & 1 & 1 & 1 & 1 & 2
\end{array} \right]
\end{array}
$$

The design is not balanced since, for example, $\lambda_{AB} = 1$ but $\lambda_{BD} = 0$.

Solution 2.4

For design 1 we obtain the following results:

(a)

$$
\mathbf{C} =
\begin{array}{c c}
 & \begin{array}{ccccccc} A & B & C & D & E & F & G \end{array} \\
\begin{array}{c} A \\ B \\ C \\ D \\ E \\ F \\ G \end{array} &
\left[\begin{array}{ccccccc}
3 & 1 & 1 & 1 & 1 & 1 & 1 \\
1 & 3 & 1 & 1 & 1 & 1 & 1 \\
1 & 1 & 3 & 1 & 1 & 1 & 1 \\
1 & 1 & 1 & 3 & 1 & 1 & 1 \\
1 & 1 & 1 & 1 & 3 & 1 & 1 \\
1 & 1 & 1 & 1 & 1 & 3 & 1 \\
1 & 1 & 1 & 1 & 1 & 1 & 3
\end{array} \right]
\end{array}
$$

(b)

$$\mathbf{B} = \begin{array}{c} \\ A \\ B \\ C \\ D \\ E \\ F \\ G \end{array}\begin{array}{ccccccc} 1 & 2 & 3 & 4 & 5 & 6 & 7 \\ \left[\begin{array}{ccccccc} 1 & 0 & 0 & 0 & 1 & 0 & 1 \\ 1 & 1 & 0 & 0 & 0 & 1 & 0 \\ 0 & 1 & 1 & 0 & 0 & 0 & 1 \\ 1 & 0 & 1 & 1 & 0 & 0 & 0 \\ 0 & 1 & 0 & 1 & 1 & 0 & 0 \\ 0 & 0 & 1 & 0 & 1 & 1 & 0 \\ 0 & 0 & 0 & 1 & 0 & 1 & 1 \end{array}\right] \end{array} \qquad \mathbf{B}^T = \begin{array}{c} \\ 1 \\ 2 \\ 3 \\ 4 \\ 5 \\ 6 \\ 7 \end{array}\begin{array}{ccccccc} A & B & C & D & E & F & G \\ \left[\begin{array}{ccccccc} 1 & 1 & 0 & 1 & 0 & 0 & 0 \\ 0 & 1 & 1 & 0 & 1 & 0 & 0 \\ 0 & 0 & 1 & 1 & 0 & 1 & 0 \\ 0 & 0 & 0 & 1 & 1 & 0 & 1 \\ 1 & 0 & 0 & 0 & 1 & 1 & 0 \\ 0 & 1 & 0 & 0 & 0 & 1 & 1 \\ 1 & 0 & 1 & 0 & 0 & 0 & 1 \end{array}\right] \end{array}$$

(c)

$$\mathbf{BB}^T = \begin{bmatrix} 1 & 0 & 0 & 0 & 1 & 0 & 1 \\ 1 & 1 & 0 & 0 & 0 & 1 & 0 \\ 0 & 1 & 1 & 0 & 0 & 0 & 1 \\ 1 & 0 & 1 & 1 & 0 & 0 & 0 \\ 0 & 1 & 0 & 1 & 1 & 0 & 0 \\ 0 & 0 & 1 & 0 & 1 & 1 & 0 \\ 0 & 0 & 0 & 1 & 0 & 1 & 1 \end{bmatrix}\begin{bmatrix} 1 & 1 & 0 & 1 & 0 & 0 & 0 \\ 0 & 1 & 1 & 0 & 1 & 0 & 0 \\ 0 & 0 & 1 & 1 & 0 & 1 & 0 \\ 0 & 0 & 0 & 1 & 1 & 0 & 1 \\ 1 & 0 & 0 & 0 & 1 & 1 & 0 \\ 0 & 1 & 0 & 0 & 0 & 1 & 1 \\ 1 & 0 & 1 & 0 & 0 & 0 & 1 \end{bmatrix} = \begin{bmatrix} 3 & 1 & 1 & 1 & 1 & 1 & 1 \\ 1 & 3 & 1 & 1 & 1 & 1 & 1 \\ 1 & 1 & 3 & 1 & 1 & 1 & 1 \\ 1 & 1 & 1 & 3 & 1 & 1 & 1 \\ 1 & 1 & 1 & 1 & 3 & 1 & 1 \\ 1 & 1 & 1 & 1 & 1 & 3 & 1 \\ 1 & 1 & 1 & 1 & 1 & 1 & 3 \end{bmatrix} = \mathbf{C}$$

For design 2 we obtain the following results:

(a)

$$\mathbf{C} = \begin{array}{c} \\ A \\ B \\ C \\ D \\ E \\ F \\ G \end{array}\begin{array}{ccccccc} A & B & C & D & E & F & G \\ \left[\begin{array}{ccccccc} 3 & 2 & 1 & 0 & 0 & 1 & 2 \\ 2 & 3 & 2 & 1 & 0 & 0 & 1 \\ 1 & 2 & 3 & 2 & 1 & 0 & 0 \\ 0 & 1 & 2 & 3 & 2 & 1 & 0 \\ 0 & 0 & 1 & 2 & 3 & 2 & 1 \\ 1 & 0 & 0 & 1 & 2 & 3 & 2 \\ 2 & 1 & 0 & 0 & 1 & 2 & 3 \end{array}\right] \end{array}$$

(b)

$$\mathbf{B} = \begin{array}{c} \\ A \\ B \\ C \\ D \\ E \\ F \\ G \end{array}\begin{array}{ccccccc} 1 & 2 & 3 & 4 & 5 & 6 & 7 \\ \left[\begin{array}{ccccccc} 1 & 0 & 0 & 0 & 0 & 1 & 1 \\ 1 & 1 & 0 & 0 & 0 & 0 & 1 \\ 1 & 1 & 1 & 0 & 0 & 0 & 0 \\ 0 & 1 & 1 & 1 & 0 & 0 & 0 \\ 0 & 0 & 1 & 1 & 1 & 0 & 0 \\ 0 & 0 & 0 & 1 & 1 & 1 & 0 \\ 0 & 0 & 0 & 0 & 1 & 1 & 1 \end{array}\right] \end{array} \qquad \mathbf{B}^T = \begin{array}{c} \\ 1 \\ 2 \\ 3 \\ 4 \\ 5 \\ 6 \\ 7 \end{array}\begin{array}{ccccccc} A & B & C & D & E & F & G \\ \left[\begin{array}{ccccccc} 1 & 1 & 1 & 0 & 0 & 0 & 0 \\ 0 & 1 & 1 & 1 & 0 & 0 & 0 \\ 0 & 0 & 1 & 1 & 1 & 0 & 0 \\ 0 & 0 & 0 & 1 & 1 & 1 & 0 \\ 0 & 0 & 0 & 0 & 1 & 1 & 1 \\ 1 & 0 & 0 & 0 & 0 & 1 & 1 \\ 1 & 1 & 0 & 0 & 0 & 0 & 1 \end{array}\right] \end{array}$$

(c)

$$\mathbf{BB}^T = \begin{bmatrix} 1 & 0 & 0 & 0 & 0 & 1 & 1 \\ 1 & 1 & 0 & 0 & 0 & 0 & 1 \\ 1 & 1 & 1 & 0 & 0 & 0 & 0 \\ 0 & 1 & 1 & 1 & 0 & 0 & 0 \\ 0 & 0 & 1 & 1 & 1 & 0 & 0 \\ 0 & 0 & 0 & 1 & 1 & 1 & 0 \\ 0 & 0 & 0 & 0 & 1 & 1 & 1 \end{bmatrix}\begin{bmatrix} 1 & 1 & 1 & 0 & 0 & 0 & 0 \\ 0 & 1 & 1 & 1 & 0 & 0 & 0 \\ 0 & 0 & 1 & 1 & 1 & 0 & 0 \\ 0 & 0 & 0 & 1 & 1 & 1 & 0 \\ 0 & 0 & 0 & 0 & 1 & 1 & 1 \\ 1 & 0 & 0 & 0 & 0 & 1 & 1 \\ 1 & 1 & 0 & 0 & 0 & 0 & 1 \end{bmatrix} = \begin{bmatrix} 3 & 2 & 1 & 0 & 0 & 1 & 2 \\ 2 & 3 & 2 & 1 & 0 & 0 & 1 \\ 1 & 2 & 3 & 2 & 1 & 0 & 0 \\ 0 & 1 & 2 & 3 & 2 & 1 & 0 \\ 0 & 0 & 1 & 2 & 3 & 2 & 1 \\ 1 & 0 & 0 & 1 & 2 & 3 & 2 \\ 2 & 1 & 0 & 0 & 1 & 2 & 3 \end{bmatrix} = \mathbf{C}$$

Solution 2.5

(a) For this design, $v = 7$, $r = 3$, $k = 3$ and $\lambda = 1$; so

$$\lambda(v-1) = 1 \times (7-1) = 1 \times 6 = 6,$$

and

$$r(k-1) = 3 \times (3-1) = 3 \times 2 = 6.$$

Thus $\lambda(v-1) = r(k-1)$.

(b) For this design, $v = 6$, $r = 5$, $k = 3$ and $\lambda = 2$; so

$$\lambda(v-1) = 2 \times (6-1) = 2 \times 5 = 10,$$

and

$$r(k-1) = 5 \times (3-1) = 5 \times 2 = 10.$$

Thus $\lambda(v-1) = r(k-1)$.

(c) For this design, $v = 8$, $r = 7$, $k = 4$ and $\lambda = 3$; so

$$\lambda(v-1) = 3 \times (8-1) = 3 \times 7 = 21,$$

and

$$r(k-1) = 7 \times (4-1) = 7 \times 3 = 21.$$

Thus $\lambda(v-1) = r(k-1)$.

Solution 2.6

If the design has v varieties and b blocks, then $vr = bk$ and $v \le b$, and so

$$k = vr/b \le br/b = r,$$

as required.

Solution 2.7

There are many possible designs — for example:

(a) design (a) of Problem 2.5;

(b) design (b) of Problem 2.5.

Solution 2.8

Suppose that there is a BIBD with $v = b = 22$ and $r = k = 7$. Then

$$\lambda = r(k-1)/(v-1) = 7 \times (7-1)/(22-1) = (7 \times 6)/21 = 2.$$

Since v is even, we can apply Theorem 2.4. But

$$r - \lambda = 7 - 2 = 5,$$

which is *not* the square of an integer. It follows that no BIBD exists with these parameters.

Solution 2.9

The dual of design 1 is

A	B	C	D	E	F	G
1	1	2	1	2	3	4
5	2	3	3	4	5	6
7	6	7	4	5	6	7

which is a balanced design with $\lambda = 1$.

Solution 2.10

By the result of Problem 1.16, if v, b, r and k are the parameters of Δ, then the parameters of Δ^* are $v^* = b$, $b^* = v$, $r^* = k$ and $k^* = r$. It follows that the concurrence λ^* of Δ^* is given by

$$\begin{aligned} \lambda^* &= r^*(k^* - 1)/(v^* - 1) \\ &= k(r-1)/(b-1) \\ &= r(k-1)/(v-1) \qquad (\Delta \text{ is symmetric, so } r = k \text{ and } v = b) \\ &= \lambda. \end{aligned}$$

Solution 2.11

Working modulo 11, we have:

(a) $4 + 9 (= 13) = 2$;

(b) $4 - 9 (= -5) = 6$;

(c) $4 \times 9 (= 36) = 3$.

Solution 2.12

Working modulo 7, we obtain the table of differences

	0	1	3
0	0	6	4
1	1	0	5
3	3	2	0

Each non-zero variety occurs once in this table, so, by Theorem 2.8, the first row of the concurrence matrix is

column	0	1	2	3	4	5	6
first row	3	1	1	1	1	1	1

By Theorem 2.7, the concurrence matrix is

	0	1	2	3	4	5	6
0	3	1	1	1	1	1	1
1	1	3	1	1	1	1	1
2	1	1	3	1	1	1	1
3	1	1	1	3	1	1	1
4	1	1	1	1	3	1	1
5	1	1	1	1	1	3	1
6	1	1	1	1	1	1	3

Solution 2.13

(a)   Working modulo 11, we obtain the table of differences

	1	3	4	5	9
1	0	9	8	7	3
3	2	0	10	9	5
4	3	1	0	10	6
5	4	2	1	0	7
9	8	6	5	4	0

Each non-zero variety occurs the same number of times — twice. Thus the set {1, 3, 4, 5, 9} is a perfect difference set.

(b)   By Theorem 2.9, we obtain the required design with $\lambda = 2$ by constructing the cyclic design with first block 1 3 4 5 9:

1	2	3	4	5	6	7	8	9	10	11
1	2	3	4	5	6	7	8	9	10	0
3	4	5	6	7	8	9	10	0	1	2
4	5	6	7	8	9	10	0	1	2	3
5	6	7	8	9	10	0	1	2	3	4
9	10	0	1	2	3	4	5	6	7	8

Solution 2.14

(a) We obtain the table of differences

	0	1	2	3
0	0	12	11	10
1	1	0	12	11
2	2	1	0	12
3	3	2	1	0

The non-zero numbers 1, 2, ... , 12 do not appear the same number of times; for example, 12 occurs three times, 3 occurs just once, and 4 does not appear at all. Thus {0, 1, 2, 3} is not a perfect difference set (modulo 13).

Note that this highly unbalanced situation occurs whenever we start with a block of consecutive numbers. This shows why the circle construction is usually undesirable.

(b) We obtain the table of differences

	0	1	4	6
0	0	12	9	7
1	1	0	10	8
4	4	3	0	11
6	6	5	2	0

The non-zero numbers 1, 2, ... , 12 appear the same number of times — once. Thus {0, 1, 4, 6} is a perfect difference set (modulo 13).

(c) We obtain the table of differences

	0	1	5	7
0	0	12	8	6
1	1	0	9	7
5	5	4	0	11
7	7	6	2	0

The non-zero numbers 1, 2, ..., 12 do not appear the same number of times; for example, 6 occurs twice, 2 occurs once, and 3 does not appear at all. Thus {0, 1, 5, 7} is not a perfect difference set (modulo 13).

Solution 2.15

(a) The non-zero squares (modulo 11) are

$$1^2 (= 10^2) = 1; \quad 2^2 (= 9^2) = 4; \quad 3^2 (= 8^2) = 9;$$
$$4^2 (= 7^2) = 5; \quad 5^2 (= 6^2) = 3;$$

that is, 1, 3, 4, 5, 9.

(b) The non-zero squares (modulo 13) are

$$1^2 (= 12^2) = 1; \quad 2^2 (= 11^2) = 4; \quad 3^2 (= 10^2) = 9;$$
$$4^2 (= 9^2) = 3; \quad 5^2 (= 8^2) = 12; \quad 6^2 (= 7^2) = 10;$$

that is, 1, 3, 4, 9, 10, 12.

Solution 2.16

The non-zero squares (modulo 19) are

$$1^2 (= 18^2) = 1; \quad 2^2 (= 17^2) = 4; \quad 3^2 (= 16^2) = 9;$$
$$4^2 (= 15^2) = 16; \quad 5^2 (= 14^2) = 6; \quad 6^2 (= 13^2) = 17;$$
$$7^2 (= 12^2) = 11; \quad 8^2 (= 11^2) = 7; \quad 9^2 (= 10^2) = 5;$$

that is, 1, 4, 5, 6, 7, 9, 11, 16, 17.

Thus, by Theorem 2.10, {1, 4, 5, 6, 7, 9, 11, 16, 17} is a perfect difference set (modulo 19).

Solution 2.17

(a) construction 2, with $p = 29$;

(b) construction 3, with $p = 29$;

(c) construction 1, with $p = 31$;

(d) construction 4, with $p = 31$.

Solution 3.1

(a) It follows from the equation $\lambda(v - 1) = r(k - 1)$ with $k = 3$ and $\lambda = 1$ that

$$v - 1 = 2r, \qquad \text{and so} \qquad r = (v - 1)/2.$$

(b) Since $r = (v - 1)/2$ is an integer, $v - 1$ must be even, and so v is odd.

(c) It now follows from the equation $vr = bk$ that

$$v(v - 1)/2 = 3b, \qquad \text{and so} \qquad b = v(v - 1)/6.$$

Solution 3.2

There are several possible solutions — for example:

Monday			Tuesday			Wednesday			Thursday		
1	4	7	1	2	3	1	2	3	1	2	3
2	5	8	4	5	6	5	6	4	6	4	5
3	6	9	7	8	9	9	7	8	8	9	7

Solution 3.3

We have

$$\lambda(v - 1) = 1 \times (n^2 + n) = (n + 1)n = r(k - 1),$$

as required.

Solution 3.4

(a) Such a design would be a projective plane of order 9, which exists by Theorem 3.3.

(b) Such a design would be a projective plane of order 10, which does not exist, as stated in the text.

(c) Such a design would be a projective plane of order 11, which exists by Theorem 3.3.

Solution 3.5

(a) There are several possibilities — for example:

A	B	C		B	A	C
B	C	A		C	B	A
C	A	B		A	C	B

(b)

1	2	3		A	C	B	D
3	1	2		C	A	D	B
2	3	1		D	B	C	A
				B	D	A	C

| (1) | | | | (2) | | | |

Solution 3.6

(a)

A	B	C	D	E	F	G	H
F	G	H	A	B	C	D	E
C	D	E	F	G	H	A	B
H	A	B	C	D	E	F	G
E	F	G	H	A	B	C	D
B	C	D	E	F	G	H	A
G	H	A	B	C	D	E	F
D	E	F	G	H	A	B	C

(b) If $r = 6$, then the fifth line is the same as the first, and so we do not obtain a latin square. This is because r and n have the common factor 2.

Solution 3.7

	0	1	2	3	4	5	6
0	0	3	6	1	5	4	2
1	3	1	4	0	2	6	5
2	6	4	2	5	1	3	0
3	1	0	5	3	6	2	4
4	5	2	1	6	4	0	3
5	4	6	3	2	0	5	1
6	2	5	0	4	3	1	6

Solution 4.1

(a) This design is resolvable; its replicates are

$$1, 4; \qquad 2, 8; \qquad 3, 7; \qquad 5, 6.$$

(b) This design is not resolvable; for example, there is no block that can be combined with block 4 to form a replicate.

Solution 4.2

In Section 3.1 we saw that in any Steiner triple system the block-size k is 3 and the number v of varieties has the form $6n + 1$ or $6n + 3$ for some integer n. By Theorem 4.1, the number v/k must be an integer. But

if $v = 6n + 1$, then $v/k = 2n + \frac{1}{3}$, which is not an integer,

and

if $v = 6n + 3$, then $v/k = 2n + 1$, which is an integer.

Thus the only values of v for which a resolvable Steiner triple system can exist are those of the form $6n + 3$.

It can be shown that a resolvable Steiner triple system with v varieties exists for every integer v of the form $6n + 3$.

Solution 4.3

We have $v = 15$, $b = 35$ and $r = 7$, and the inequality becomes

$$35 \geq 15 + 7 - 1, \quad \text{or} \quad 35 \geq 21.$$

Solution 4.4

We first write the varieties in a 5 × 5 square array in any order, such as

A	B	C	D	E
F	G	H	I	J
K	L	M	N	O
P	Q	R	S	T
U	V	W	X	Y

The blocks of the first replicate are the rows of this square array:

1	2	3	4	5
A	F	K	P	U
B	G	L	Q	V
C	H	M	R	W
D	I	N	S	X
E	J	O	T	Y

The blocks of the second replicate are the columns of the array:

6	7	8	9	10
A	B	C	D	E
F	G	H	I	J
K	L	M	N	O
P	Q	R	S	T
U	V	W	X	Y

The blocks of the third replicate are the diagonals of the array:

11	12	13	14	15
A	B	C	D	E
G	H	I	J	F
M	N	O	K	L
S	T	P	Q	R
Y	U	V	W	X

Combining these replicates, we obtain the following triple lattice design:

1	2	3	4	5	6	7	8	9	10	11	12	13	14	15
A	F	K	P	U	A	B	C	D	E	A	B	C	D	E
B	G	L	Q	V	F	G	H	I	J	G	H	I	J	F
C	H	M	R	W	K	L	M	N	O	M	N	O	K	L
D	I	N	S	X	P	Q	R	S	T	S	T	P	Q	R
E	J	O	T	Y	U	V	W	X	Y	Y	U	V	W	X
replicate 1					replicate 2					replicate 3				

Solution 4.5

We write down the 20 varieties in a 5×5 square array, omitting the main diagonal:

–	A	B	C	D
E	–	F	G	H
I	J	–	K	L
M	N	O	–	P
Q	R	S	T	–

Taking the rows as the blocks of the first replicate, and the columns as the blocks of the second replicate, we obtain the following design.

1	2	3	4	5	6	7	8	9	10
A	E	I	M	Q	E	A	B	C	D
B	F	J	N	R	I	J	F	G	H
C	G	K	O	S	M	N	O	K	L
D	H	L	P	T	Q	R	S	T	P

Solution 4.6

We have $v = 8$ and $k = 2$, so $s = 4$ and $s - k = 2$; we therefore write the varieties in a 4×4 square, omitting two diagonals.

(a) If we omit two neighbouring diagonals, the array becomes

–	–	1	2
3	–	–	4
5	6	–	–
–	7	8	–

and the design is

1	2	3	4	5	6	7	8
1	3	5	7	3	6	1	2
2	4	6	8	5	7	8	4

replicate 1   replicate 2

(b) If we omit two alternate diagonals, the array becomes:

–	1	–	2
3	–	4	–
–	5	–	6
7	–	8	–

and the design is

1	2	3	4	5	6	7	8
1	3	5	7	3	1	4	2
2	4	6	8	7	5	8	6

replicate 1   replicate 2

The second of these designs is not connected, since blocks 1, 3, 6 and 8 contain only varieties 1, 2, 5 and 6, and blocks 2, 4, 5 and 7 contain only varieties 3, 4, 7 and 8.

The first design is connected, and is therefore preferable.

Solution 4.7

(a)

A	B	C	D
D	C	B	A
B	A	D	C
C	D	A	B

(b) letter A appears in positions 1, 8, 10 and 15, so we take these numbers as the varieties in block 17;

letter B appears in positions 2, 7, 9 and 16, so we take these numbers as the varieties in block 18;

letter C appears in positions 3, 6, 12 and 13, so we take these numbers as the varieties in block 19;

letter D appears in positions 4, 5, 11 and 14, so we take these numbers as the varieties in block 20.

1	2	3	4
5	6	7	8
9	10	11	12
13	14	15	16

square array

We thus obtain the replicate

17	18	19	20
1	2	3	4
8	7	6	5
10	9	12	11
15	16	13	14

Solution 5.1

For design 1 we obtain the following results.

(a) $v = b = 7, r = k = 3, \lambda = 1$.

(b) The incidence matrix is

$$
\begin{array}{c}
 \\ A \\ B \\ C \\ D \\ E \\ F \\ G
\end{array}
\begin{array}{cccccccc}
1 & 2 & 3 & 4 & 5 & 6 & 7 \\
\left[\begin{array}{ccccccc}
1 & 0 & 0 & 0 & 1 & 0 & 1 \\
1 & 1 & 0 & 0 & 0 & 1 & 0 \\
0 & 1 & 1 & 0 & 0 & 0 & 1 \\
1 & 0 & 1 & 1 & 0 & 0 & 0 \\
0 & 1 & 0 & 1 & 1 & 0 & 0 \\
0 & 0 & 1 & 0 & 1 & 1 & 0 \\
0 & 0 & 0 & 1 & 0 & 1 & 1
\end{array}\right]
\end{array}
$$

The codewords are therefore

1000101, 1100010, 0110001, 1011000,
0101100, 0010110, 0001011.

(c) The Hamming distance is $2(r - \lambda) = 2(3 - 1) = 4$.

(d) This code detects up to two errors and corrects up to one error.

For design 2 we obtain the following results.

(a) $v = 9, b = 12, r = 4, k = 3, \lambda = 1$.

(b)   The incidence matrix is

	1	2	3	4	5	6	7	8	9	10	11	12
A	1	0	0	1	0	0	1	0	0	1	0	0
B	0	1	0	0	1	0	0	1	0	1	0	0
C	0	0	1	0	0	1	0	0	1	1	0	0
D	1	0	0	0	0	1	0	1	0	0	1	0
E	0	1	0	1	0	0	0	0	1	0	1	0
F	0	0	1	0	1	0	1	0	0	0	1	0
G	1	0	0	0	1	0	0	0	1	0	0	1
H	0	1	0	0	0	1	1	0	0	0	0	1
I	0	0	1	1	0	0	0	1	0	0	0	1

The codewords are therefore

100100100100, 010010010100, 001001001100,

100001010010, 010100001010, 001010100010,

100010001001, 010001100001, 001100010001.

(c)   The Hamming distance is $2(r - \lambda) = 2(4 - 1) = 6$.

(d)   This code detects up to three errors and corrects up to two errors.

Solution 5.2

(a)   The Hamming distance is

$$2(r - \lambda) = 2((p - 1)/2 - (p - 3)/4) = (p + 1)/2 = 2n + 2,$$

so the code detects up to $n + 1$ errors and corrects up to n errors.

(b)   The Hamming distance is

$$2(r - \lambda) = 2((p - 1) - (p - 3)/2) = p + 1 = 4n + 2,$$

so the code detects up to $2n + 1$ errors and corrects up to $2n$ errors.

Solution 5.3

(a)   Take the design in Problem 5.2(b) with $p = 17$ and $n = 4$;

the code detects up to 9 errors and corrects up to 8 errors.

(b)   Take the code in Problem 5.2(a) with $p = 19$ and $n = 4$;

the code detects up to 5 errors and corrects up to 4 errors.

Index